Journeying With Jesus
Through the Basics

Journeying With Jesus
Through the Basics

a Bible Study Workbook

"Great are the works of the LORD;
they are studied by all who delight in them."

Psalm 111:2

Conni Hudson

Journeying With Jesus
42335 Washington Street, Ste F, #120
Palm Desert, CA 92211
journeyingwithjesus@gmail.com

Journeying With Jesus Logo artwork by Susan Dole
Journeying With Jesus Trademark by Conni Hudson
Cover Design by Dawn Ivie and Conni Hudson
Publishing assistance by Avant Studios, Palm Desert, CA

NOTE: Every effort has been made to locate the owners of copyrighted materials in this publication. Upon notification, the Publisher will make proper correction in subsequent printings.

ISBN 978-0-9794858-0-0

First Printing, 2007, printed in Hong Kong

Printed by
Living Stone Publishers Ltd.

Journeying With Jesus Through the Basics
© 2007 Conni Hudson
Published by *Journeying With Jesus* Ministries
42335 Washington Street, Ste F, #120
Palm Desert, CA 92211

Email address for orders and correspondence - journeyingwithjesus@gmail.com

This book is dedicated to Mary Stewart
who "prayed much and pushed gently" every step of the way.
And to those precious women at the *Journeying With Jesus* retreat
who asked for this book to be birthed – here you go!
May it be used of God to help His children grow.

Journeying With Jesus

Through the Basics

Table of Contents

FOREWORD

Two lonely, discouraged men were walking on the road from Jerusalem back to their home in Emmaus. They had just witnessed the crucifixion of the One they believed to be the Messiah. Disillusioned, discouraged, and confused about life, they were met by a stranger who asked them what they were talking about. They poured their hearts out to this One Who questioned them. Arriving at their home, they invited Him to stay with them and share a meal. As they sat down at the table together, this stranger blessed the bread, broke it, and the eyes of those two men were opened to discover the true identity of their traveling companion—it was Jesus, the One whom they had hoped was their Redeemer. In an instant, they realized He was everything they had looked for and so much more. He was the fulfillment of all Moses and the Prophets had written about: He was their Savior, their Redeemer, and the Blessed Hope of eternal life. More than that, when He met them on their road of discouragement, He opened up the Scriptures to them concerning Himself, and, as a result, He set their hearts on fire. The fire in their heart was so contagious, it spread. And it is still spreading today.

The Lord wants to set your heart on fire as well, burning with a love that will spread throughout the world. How can this happen? The Lord is inviting you to embark on an incredible journey – the great adventure of knowing Him. You hold in your hands a Bible Study Workbook, *Journeying With Jesus Through the Basics*, that is going to take you on a journey with Jesus *Through the Basics* of the Christian life—these are what life is all about. And my encouragement to you would be to never step away from the basics—stay in the meat of these 'basics' and just go deeper and deeper into understanding them and living them out in your own life until you are face-to-Face with Jesus. *Journeying With Jesus Through the Basics*, written by Conni Hudson, is a journey you can take over and over again.

I have known Conni Hudson for ten years. When I met her, I knew I had found a friend for life. She has a heart that longs to know Jesus and be intimate with Him. She loves the Bible and knows what it says from cover to cover. Her knowledge of the Bible is extraordinary and this, along with her reliance on the Holy Spirit as her strength, makes her an amazing and powerful teacher of the Word of God. She has taught the Bible for many years and speaks at retreats and conferences. One of her greatest gifts is encouragement and exhortation and you will sense her cheering you on in your own race through every page of *Journeying With Jesus Through the Basics*. She has been my cheerleader these last ten years and has encouraged me in the writing of all my books. In fact, she has led most of the pilot studies of the ten books I've written. She is a Proverbs 31 woman and it may be said of her: *Many daughters have done nobly, but you excel them all* (Proverbs 31:29).

Conni shares my passion for God and His Word. You will discover who Jesus is, what He does, and what He says only as you open your own Bible and live in it. *Journeying With Jesus Through the Basics* will help you study the Bible each day. This amazing Bible Study is called a workbook but it is truly much more than that—it is a treasure chest, waiting to be opened by you—and when you bravely begin to lift the cover and engage in the journey—you are going to discover nuggets of gold in the Psalms, jewels in the hymns, pearls of wisdom in the illustrations, and rare coins as you walk with Jesus in the Word. When you complete this journey, you will be rich indeed! What an incredible opportunity you now have to engage in the great adventure with Conni Hudson as your guide leading you into an amazing journey with the King of Kings and Lord of Lords, Jesus Himself. May you draw near to your Lord Jesus, so intimate with Him that as He leads you on the path of life, you won't just walk, but your heart will dance with Him. God bless you as you continue on in this great adventure of knowing Him.

Catherine Martin
Founder and President
Quiet Time Ministries

PREFACE TO

Journeying With Jesus
Through the Basics

Are you ready for an adventure – the adventure of the discovery of the Basics in God's Word – the discovery of what it means to be a Christian? *Journeying With Jesus **Through the Basics*** is simply a tool. It will help you discover, for yourself, the Basics of the Bible concerning Jesus Christ, how to live as a follower of Christ, and reach the journey's destination – heaven.

You may use this study tool alone or with a group. I suggest you gather with a group (2 or 200 smiley faces), so you can gain biblical insight from one another. However, remember – you plus God makes a group. Either way, He is longing to reveal Himself to you through His Word, and this study tool will help you travel through the Bible in a simple, step-by-step method.

There are eight weeks of study, each having its own theme. Then, the week is divided into five days of study, each day focusing on one aspect of the week's theme. These lessons are not conclusive, in-depth, dissertations on the theme, but simply introducing the *basics*.

You will notice there is a pattern to each week's lesson. In them you will be WALKING WITH HIM THROUGH THE WORD, WALKING WITH OTHERS, WALKING IN PRAYER, WALKING IN THE PSALMS, WALKING IN WONDER, and WALKING THROUGH TODAY: Journaling the Journey.

WALKING WITH HIM THROUGH THE WORD is your Bible Study time. You will be discovering for yourself what God's Word has to say about each theme. This leads to WALKING WITH OTHERS which is a short summary of the lesson, along with occasional quotes by others, giving further insight into the subject. Always, when you study God's Word, it should lead to a response of prayer, so you will be WALKING IN PRAYER. There you will respond to what you have just studied. WALKING IN THE PSALMS is the privilege of walking through what has been called "God's Hymn Book" – the book of Psalms. Each day you will have a Psalm that in some way speaks to the theme being studied. This is time for you to meditate on Scripture, examining how to apply what you have just studied and learned.

So often while studying, questions will arise that are not answered in the lesson, so there is WALKING IN WONDER. This is a place to note all those questions you might have from the week's lesson. We would like to answer those for you during or after class. Be sure to note any questions you might have in this section.

Finally, as you are studying or going through the lesson with a class, there may be added insights and prayers you would like to add to your day's lesson, so you can note them in WALKING THROUGH TODAY: Journaling the Journey. This is also a good place to record any notes you might want to make from the lecture.

This gives you a full day's study on a particular topic from the Bible. Each lesson is not all-encompassing, but it certainly gets you started by showing you the facts given in God's Word. Just follow the instructions each day and enjoy. Along with each week's study there is a teaching on CD to help with your understanding of the lesson.

There are many translations of the Bible. The New American Standard Bible (NASB) is used to form this study guide, as it is the translation used at the *Journeying With Jesus* retreats. The New King James Version (NKJV), and English Standard Version (ESV) are also excellent translations. The one you use is up to you. Just remember if you use a Bible other than the NASB you may notice phrases worded differently in the passage mentioned, so you might have to look for synonyms. You will want to avoid using a paraphrase version of the Bible, such as *The Message* or *The Living Bible*, though, when doing a Bible study. While you may enjoy a paraphrased Bible in your reading time, it is not a true translation (i.e. word for word, or thought for thought) and as such, is not adequate for actual study, research, or analysis of the Bible.

Also, as you are doing your lesson each day, please remember my motto: "Do your best and leave the rest." You may not be able to answer each and every question. That's O.K. Just keep going and don't give up. Answer what you can. Through the class discussion time and lecture, all the answers should be covered.

For those of you who may want to go through this study with a friend or group of friends, there is a Leader's Guide available. Please contact *Journeying With Jesus* Ministries to order a copy.

As you go through this workbook, you will find I have occasionally quoted the writings of others that speak to the subject being studied. Please understand, while approving that particular quote, I am not endorsing all of that person's writings.

I pray you will enjoy the adventure and will be blessed by the journey.

All for His glory,

Conni

Conni Hudson

ACKNOWLEDGEMENTS

I am filled with much joy and gratitude for all who labored with me to walk this book into published form.

Thank you to my husband and my best friend, Ken. Your willingness to "share me," so I could write was just the encouragement needed. You're the best! I love you! And to my children - Stacie Burns, Michelle Miller, Drew and Leah Hudson - I am grateful. Each of you, in unique ways, cheered me on, and I thank and love you more than you can imagine. To my mama, Patsy Chadwick and my aunt, Myra Blackerby...to the moon and back!

Thank you to the *Journeying With Jesus* Ministry Team: Sheila Chadwick, Diane Conklin, Diane Flannery, Dawn Ivie, Mary Stewart, Rhonda Stewart, and Julie Wingfield. What can I say? We did it! Dawn, this book would never have "been" without your hours and hours of work – a huge thank you. And a big thank you to the JWJ class who piloted this study: Mary Butterfield, Sheila Chadwick, Diane Conklin, Cheryl Davis, Susan Dole, Diane Flannery, Dawn Ivie, Jan Mander, Olivia Smith, Mary Stewart, Rhonda Stewart, Julie Wingfield, and Delores Zuber. Your input was invaluable.

Thank you to my dear friends at Quiettime Ministries: Kelly Abeyratne, Julie Airis, Kayla Branscum, Cindy Clark, Catherine Martin, Shirley Peters, Shelley Smith, and Paula Zilmer, who prayed, encouraged, and helped in every way. Kayla, you are a wonder!

Thank you to the New Life Community Church, especially the women's prayer group: Nancy Brown, Sheila Chadwick, Cheryl Clarke, Jean Gunderson, Penney Jennings, Joan Hill, Kay McCann, Kate Storset, and Patty Zachary. You always remembered to pray!

Thank you to my Biblical Counseling Foundation friends and colleagues in the work of discipleship: Bob Schneider, Shashi Smith, Stuart Smith, Spencer Smith, and the office staff -my deepest gratitude for your servant's hearts.

And thank you to my teachers, who taught me the "basics" and more: Deanna Campbell (my spiritual mother), Ellen Bingham (my Bible Study Fellowship Teacher), Joyce Hall (my Community Bible Study Leader), Shashi Smith and Bob Schneider (my Biblical Counseling Foundation instructors), Kay Arthur (Precept Ministries author and teacher), Catherine Martin (Quiettime Ministries founder and teacher), and my pastor, Jon Skramstad (New Life Community Church) who teaches the Word faithfully each week.

And to all my friends who have prayed, served, and loved me out of their love for Jesus. How can I ever thank you enough?

If I have forgotten anyone, it was not intentional. The Lord has blessed me with family and friends who love me beyond measure and who pray for the Lord to be glorified through this work. To you all I say thank you from the bottom of my heart.

Above all, I thank God the Father and the Lord Jesus Christ for choosing, calling, and saving me, and for the Holy Spirit's guidance into all truth. TO GOD BE THE GLORY!

Eternally gratefully,

Conni Hudson

INTRODUCTION

I have a friend who is what we call, "directionally impaired." She has a hard time getting from point A to point B. Since she understands her plight, she keeps a binder of maps in her car. And because I know this about her, when we go places together, I point and direct. As her friend, I have become her tour guide, not only keeping her going in the right direction but pointing out the interesting sights along the way. That's what I want to do for you. Since Jesus has commissioned us, not only to share the good news of the gospel but also to come alongside others to teach them how to walk in Him and with Him, I want to help you get from point A to point B in knowing and understanding the Bible and the Jesus of the Bible. This is what God calls discipleship (see Matthew 28:19-20).

I have been *journeying with Jesus* for 26 years now. We've made some steep, up-hill climbs - I struggled as He cheered me on. We've come to bends in the road I was afraid to make - He waited patiently. We've walked through the valley of the shadow of death - I mourned and He comforted. We've strolled through meadows filled with wild flowers - I sang for joy as He smiled in delight. We've been through dark places where the sun was shrouded by cloud - I could not see to walk, so He carried me.

During all of our journeying together, Jesus has had someone come alongside to hold my other hand - someone to walk with me and be my tour guide. Now, I would like to be yours. I will take your other hand and as you are *journeying with Jesus*, I'll walk along side and point out the sights. You really don't need me, you need only Him, but He has called us to share with one another in the grand journey. And I am so happy for the privilege of walking together with you!

"Great are the works of the LORD;
they are studied by all who delight in them."

Psalm 111:2

Section A

Journeying to Eternity

Section A
Journeying to Eternity

Week One

The Eternal Plan

Day One   Living with Eternity in Mind

Day Two   God's Plan for Eternity

Day Three   Created for Himself: The Eternal

Day Four   The Aim of Eternity

Day Five   The Promise of Eternity

Living with Eternity in Mind

Now set your heart and soul to seek the Lord your God...
1 Chronicles 22:19

 ## Walking with Him through the Word

"I think I've discovered something" the man exclaimed as he walked into my friend's office. She was anxious to hear about his "aha moment." As he sat down and began to talk, she could see a difference in him, a determination. "I've been to two funerals of acquaintances in this past week. The first service was for a man who was religious in the sense that he went to church regularly, gave to worthy causes, and was a good provider for his family. The service was all about his business and educational accomplishments, his grand vacations, and great golf games. In fact, the remark was made something to the effect he was 'up in heaven playing his greatest golf game ever.' I left feeling miserable and humming the tune to Peggy Lee's golden-oldie, *Is That All There Is?*

What a contrast the second funeral was! This man's service was a celebration of his love for, and trust in, Christ Jesus. It was awesome! The family shared how he made all his decisions based on what Christ would want him to do and how he taught them to look to Christ for their direction. They smiled through their tears as they spoke of his being with the Lord, at home in heaven. The focus of the service reflected his life's focus – **he lived with eternity in mind.**

This was an "aha moment" for this man. "I realized this life is not all there is, and living is not about accomplishments or failure to accomplish the world's goals. Neither is it about looking to the world for approval. Life is all about eternity! All that matters are the eternal things –not striving to keep up with and surpass "the Joneses" nor finding one's passion or purpose in the things of the world. Life is about the things and Person of Eternity."

At last, this man grasped the truth and had come to my friend with the question he knew she could answer: "How do I live with eternity in mind?"

Old Testament Scripture:

1. Read Deuteronomy 4:29. What is the focus of our life to be?

2. How does I Chronicles 16:11 show us this is to be a lifestyle, a lifelong goal?

3. According to I Chronicles 22:19, when King David was giving instructions to build the temple of God in Israel to his son, Solomon, what exhortation did he give Solomon concerning his focus?

4. In I Chronicles 28:9, how does David explain to Solomon what it means to seek God? What would be the result of his choices? What does David tell Solomon about God?

New Testament Scripture:

5. In Matthew 6:32-33, what are you to seek? What are you to do, and what is the result?

6. Read John 1:1, 14, and 17. Who is the Person of Eternity you are to seek?

7. What does Jesus say about Himself in John 14:6-7?

8. What promise does He give in John 14:23?

9. What does loving God mean for the Christian live?

Walking with Others

A.W. Tozer put it this way, "We are called to an everlasting preoccupation with God." Seeking Him is the lifestyle of the Christian. It is living with eternity in mind. All we think, do, and say comes from our relationship with God. When we seek Him, we find Him by faith in Christ and thus begins a life-journey of seeking God – discovering through His Word, creation, prayer, and the circumstances of life Who He is, how He loves and cares for us now as He walks us to our eternal home and the unspeakable joys to be found with Him there. What a journey and adventure is eternal life!!!

~~~~~~

> The evil habit of seeking **God**-'**and**' ['**and**' being anything else such as God **and** power, God **and** fame, God **and** money, God **and** popularity] effectively prevents us from finding God in full revelation. In the 'and' lies our great woe. If we omit the 'and', we will soon find God, and in Him we shall find that for which we have all our lives been secretly longing.
>
> A.W. Tozer in *The Pursuit of God*[1]

Walking In Prayer

Have you set your heart to seek the Lord? Are you living with eternity in mind? Do you know He loves you and is waiting just for you? He wants to live with you in a close, abiding relationship that begins the moment you invite Him to come into your life. You will find the One whom you have been seeking and will discover He's been waiting for you. In fact, He put it in your heart to seek Him. And if you have already asked Him into your life, are you living with eternity in mind? Are you seeking to please Him with all your being?

Pray and ask God to give you a heart that seeks after Him, to help you today to live with eternity in mind.

Walking in the Psalms

Read and meditate on Psalm 34. List everything you learn about the Lord, seeking Him, and the resulting blessings. (To meditate on Scripture means to ponder, to slowly think it over.)

THE LORD	SEEKING HIM	RESULTING BLESSINGS

 ## Walking in Wonder

Make a note of any unanswered questions you would like to have covered in class or may want to ask your teacher privately. If you don't write them down, you might forget what you wanted to ask. And remember, if you wondered about it, someone else may be wondering, too. That's why we study together – to help one another discover and understand God's truth. It's a "team effort."

Walking Through Today: Journaling the Journey

_____

_____

_____

_____

_____

_____

_____

_____

_____

_____

_____

_____

_____

_____

_____

_____

_____

_____

_____

_____

Walking Through Today: Journaling the Journey   Date:_____

Walking Through Today: Journaling the Journey

God's Plan for Eternity

...God He has also set eternity in their heart...
Ecclesiastes 3:11

 ## Walking with Him through the Word

Ecclesiastes 3:11 tells us "**God...has also set eternity in their heart.**" This shows us God has always planned for our eternal relationship with Him. What an incredible truth! He planned to provide for our relationship with Him **from eternity** and **to eternity**. How do we know? His eternal Word tells us and explains His plan to us. The Bible explains the history of His plan, progressively revealed as people throughout the ages have walked with Him. We see His plan for relationship with us from eternity past to eternity future.

Genesis, the Book of Beginnings, tells us how our love relationship with God began and was broken. He began it by creating us.

Old Testament Scripture

1. Read Genesis 1:1, 27, 31 to discover the creation by God of man and woman. What did God say about His creation?

2. According to Genesis 1:28-30 and Genesis 2:8-9, 15 after God created mankind, how did He provide for them?

3. What one restrictive command did God give them with what consequence (see Genesis 2:16-17)?

4. According to Genesis 3:6 did they obey God?

This is the biblical, and therefore accurate, account of how sin entered into the realm of mankind. The relationship between God and man was broken. The innocence of man was forever marred, and from that point on, everyone born into the world would be born in the image of Adam (see Genesis 5:1): born physically with a body that would surely decay and die, born separated from God (spiritually dead) and separated eternally unless a way of salvation was provided for them. Let's look up some Scriptures to see what God's plan was to restore mankind to relationship with Himself.

New Testament Scripture

5. Read Romans 5:8-11. How did God provide for our eternity?

6. According to Romans 5:21, God's plan for eternity would come through whom? What would be the result?

7. Read Ephesians 1:4 and note when God planned for our eternal relationship?

8. <u>Turn to Revelation, the book that reveals "the rest of the story," and read 21:1-5 and 22:1-5</u>. <u>This is a glimpse into eternity with God</u>. <u>We will be there with our Lord forever</u>. <u>Note what it will be like, what we will do, and especially what our relationship with God will be like</u>.

9. <u>Did you notice, there is a tree there that was also in the Garden of Eden at the beginning? Which tree is it?</u>

After man sinned, he was forbidden to eat of the tree of life. He was also removed from the Garden of Eden and an angel was set guard over it to prevent him from eating of the tree of life and living forever in a decaying body. This was the mercy of God. In eternity future, this tree will be in heaven and all will be able to eat of its fruit, for we will have bodies without sin's stain and so live forever! Hallelujah! What a God! He thinks of everything!

 Walking with Others

The reality is - the truth is - God created us for eternity. He put eternity in our hearts, so we would realize there is more than what we see and what this life has to offer. He put eternity in our hearts because it is in His heart. He created us to have an eternal relationship of love, joy, and peace with Him. Even before sin broke our relationship with Him, He provided a plan for us to be restored to Him, so we can begin our eternal relationship with Him now. And He has planned for eternity with us in mind. Our home is prepared and waiting for the grand, glorious day we'll be together with Him forever.

Walking in Prayer

How does knowing God planned for eternity with you before the world was ever created impact you? What things stand out to you from these truths? Write a prayer to the Lord, praising Him for the truths He revealed to you today.

Walking in the Psalms

Read and meditate on Psalm 111. As you read, underline the key-repeated word, 'forever' in your Bible. List everything you learn about 'forever' below. How do you see eternity in this Psalm?

 Walking in Wonder

Don't forget to jot down any unanswered questions you might have from this day's study.

Walking Through Today: Journaling the Journey

_____

_____

_____

_____

_____

_____

_____

_____

_____

_____

_____

_____

_____

_____

_____

_____

_____

_____

_____

_____

_____

_____

_____

_____

_____

_____

_____

_____

_____

_____

_____

_____

_____

_____

_____

_____

_____

_____

_____

_____

_____

Walking Through Today: Journaling the Journey   Date:_____

Walking Through Today: Journaling the Journey

Created For Himself: The Eternal

Glory and honor to God forever and ever.
He is the eternal King, the unseen one who never dies;
He alone is God. Amen.
I Timothy 1:17

 ## Walking with Him through the Word

"Grandma, tell me a story about when you were little." My granddaughter asks this question of me almost every time we are together. I laugh because I asked the same question of my grandma and still ask my mother, aunts, and uncles. I want to know my family. I want to know the family history so I can grasp an understanding of who they were by what they did and said. This creates intimacy, security, belonging.

The same is true of our God. If life is all about eternity, and we are to live with eternity in mind – seeking the God of eternity so we can walk in an intimate relationship with Him – then we must ask the questions of discovery, so we can know Him. This will increase our realization of security and belonging. Since our relationship with God is spiritual and not physical, then we must go to the one place where the history of God's family is recorded – the Word of God. Let's go through some Scriptures together, letting it tell us a story about God our Father, the Person of Eternity. It will be like putting a puzzle together, as it is when we hear all the "grandma stories" of our family histories.

Old Testament Scripture:

1. <u>From Genesis 1:1, what is the first thing we learn about God?</u>

The rest of the chapter tells us how God created the heavens and the earth in six days. What a story of our beginning! God's Word tells us we were created on the sixth day, after He had created an environment in which we could live. Thank You, Lord!

<u>How does Exodus 20:11 reiterate this truth?</u>

2. Write out the verse, Genesis 1:26. Who is the "us" and "our" in this verse? To Whom is God speaking? (Don't answer now -keep studying and come back to this question later.)

3. What does Deuteronomy 4:35 and 39 tell you about God?

4. In Psalm 68:5, Who does He say He is to believers (as a family member)?

New Testament Scripture:

5. In John 1:1-3, how is Jesus described?

6. According to John 1:17-18, Who came to reveal the Father by His words and life?

7. According to John 14:16-18, when Jesus was getting ready to go back to heaven to be with the Father, Who did He promise to send to be with believers always? Notice in verse 18, Who He says is going to come to them.

8. Now, go back to the top of the lesson and answer the question, Who is the "we" in Genesis 1:26?

9. What does knowing the Person of Eternity is your Creator, Lord, Father, Savior, and Counselor mean to you today?

Walking with Others

The Person of Eternity is God. He is One God. He is God in Three Persons, whom we call the Trinity. The Trinity is made up of God the Father, God the Son, and God the Holy Spirit. The character qualities of God the Father are found in the Son and the Spirit, for each is God. However, they have different roles in the eternal plan of our relationship with God. The Father sent the Son to physically explain Who God is – His holiness, love, justice, purity, etc. The Son's role, also, was to reveal God's love by dying for our sins and paying the debt we owed. And, God raised Him from the dead, thus proving the Son was Who He said He was, the payment was accepted according to the plan. The Holy Spirit's role is to indwell believers, illuminate God's Word to their hearts so they are counseled by the Lord as God is walking them to their eternal home, heaven. *Journeying with Jesus* is walking in Him and with Him in a close, personal, spiritual relationship from the time you accept Him as Savior and Lord throughout all eternity. He is the Person of Eternity.

~~~~~~~~~~~~~~~~~~~~~~~~~~~~~~~~~~~~~~

Any one of you may hold your hand before you and look at it. Between your eye and your hand are three things which are one, and which are also three. Each may be studied separately, but it is impossible to have one without the others. Between your hand and your eye at this moment are light and heat and air. Your eye can see your hand because of the light waves that are in the visible spectrum. Even when there is no visible light, there are invisible rays below the red and beyond the violet - infrared and ultraviolet. Darkness is only a matter of human eyes - that which stimulates the rods and cones of our retina we call visible light; the rest, no less real, is invisible light.

Before you in the light that you see there is also air. If you blow on your hand you can feel the air. You breathe it in; you breathe it out. You live by it. And there is heat between you and your hand; take a thermometer and measure it - see its variations as you go from a warm room to the winter snow without. You cannot have heat, or light, without having them in some relationship to our atmosphere. And you cannot have heat or air without having them in some relationship to our atmosphere. Science can use any one of them apart from the others, but can never separate them totally. To all intents and purposes they are three, and they are one.

We Christians do not believe that there are three Gods, but that there is one true God who is in three persons.

Donald Gray Barnhouse in *Let Me Illustrate*[2]

Walking in Prayer

Won't you spend some time in prayer, praising God the Father for His perfect plan of eternity which included His creation of you? And won't you thank Him for sending God the Son to reveal Himself to you and for the indwelling Spirit Who illuminates the way? Write out your prayer below to help you articulate your thoughts.

Walking in the Psalms

Please read Psalm 145 today. Make a list of the qualities of God you discover. Then praise Him for who He is – the Person of Eternity.

Walking in Wonder

Be sure to note any unanswered questions – the "I wonder..." questions, so they can be addressed in class.

Walking Through Today: Journaling the Journey

_____

_____

_____

_____

_____

_____

_____

_____

_____

_____

_____

_____

_____

_____

_____

_____

_____

_____

_____

_____

_____

Walking Through Today: Journaling the Journey   Date:_____

The Aim of Eternity
So our aim is to please him always...
II Corinthians 5:9

 ## Walking with Him through the Word

Do you enjoy reading? Have you read <u>A Chance to Die – the Life and Legacy of Amy Carmichael</u> by Elizabeth Elliott? Or <u>Created for Commitment</u> by A. Wetherell Johnson? Or <u>Ruth, A Portrait</u> by Patricia Cornwell? I mention these three, because they tell the remarkable stories of the lives of women who lived with eternity in mind. Each woman had one aim in life: to know and live for her Lord. And because her aim (her will) was God's own will for her, she reached her goal and left a legacy of faithfulness to encourage we who are following behind.

What is the aim of your life? What should it be? Stop now and pray for the Lord to open your eyes to realize His true aim for you. You may write your prayer here or on your journal pages.

Old Testament Scripture:

1. <u>Read Psalm 46:10. What are you to do?</u>

2. <u>Read Psalm 100:3. What are you to know?</u>

Aren't you at times busy, distracted, disturbed? The Lord calls you to settle down and realize He is there and He is God. He's your Creator and He cares for you as a shepherd does his sheep.

3. <u>According to Psalm 27:4, what is the psalmist's one aim in life?</u>

4. <u>Read Ezra 7:9-10. What was Ezra's one aim?</u>

<u>How does his aim fit with the aim to know God?</u>

New Testament Scripture:

5. <u>From Colossians 1:9-10, what was Paul's prayer for the believers?</u> <u>What would be the results?</u>

Paul's prayer is for your aim (focus) to be on eternity.

6. <u>Read Philippians 3:8-14.</u> <u>How did Paul further describe his one aim in life?</u>

<u>How did all else compare?</u>

<u>Had he reached his goal?</u>

<u>What did he do in order to reach it?</u>

You have been studying long and hard.
Can you handle a little more – it's really insightful!

7. Hebrews 11 is the often called the Hall of Faith. It is a list of men and women whose aim in life was to know God, so they lived with eternity in mind. Read the chapter, note the person, and the result of their having lived for the one aim of knowing and pleasing God.

Person	Result

[continue on reverse side]

Person	Result

8. <u>As the book of your life is being written, what legacy are you leaving? What things need to be changed today in order to leave a legacy of faithfulness for those following you?</u>

 Walking with Others

Through all the examples of the believers who have gone before, the outstanding truth for each life is he or she had one aim: to know intimately the Lord and live to please Him. Each person lived with eternity in mind, giving and focusing their life on God. Our lives can be no different. As we narrow our goal to Christ and Christ alone, we discover true life – eternal life - is the grandest adventure and is freedom indeed.

~~~~~~

Father, I want to know Thee, but my cowardly heart fears to give up its toys. I cannot part with them without inward bleeding, and I do not try to hide from Thee the terror of the parting. I come trembling, but I do come. Please root from my heart all those things which I have cherished so long and which have become a very part of my living self, so that Thou mayest enter and dwell there without a rival. Then shalt Thou make the place of Thy feet glorious. Then shall my heart have no need of the sun to shine in it, for Thyself wilt be the light of it, and there shall be no night there. In Jesus' name, Amen.

A. W. Tozer in *The Pursuit of God* [3]

~~~~~~

…Jesus is the solitary aim of our soul, and His glory without any additions whatever, is the end of all our efforts.

Charles Haddon Spurgeon in *Morning and Evening* [4]

Walking in Prayer

After meditating on all you've studied today and reading Tozer's prayer, how has the Lord spoken to your heart today? Won't you respond in prayer? Tell Him all that is on your heart for He loves to listen. *"The eyes of the Lord are on the righteous; and His ears are open to their cry"* (Psalm 34:15).

Walking in the Psalms

Read Psalm 27. How did the psalmist's one aim affect his attitude and his actions?

Walking in Wonder

I was wondering …

Walking Through Today: Journaling the Journey

_____

_____

_____

_____

_____

_____

_____

_____

_____

_____

_____

_____

_____

_____

_____

_____

_____

_____

_____

_____

_____

_____

_____

_____

_____

_____

Walking Through Today: Journaling the Journey   Date:_____

Walking Through Today: Journaling the Journey

The Promise of Eternity

I will be your God throughout your lifetime--until your hair is white with age.
I made you, and I will care for you. I will carry you along and save you.
Isaiah 46:4

 Walking With Him through the Word

When I was a little girl, my sister, brother, and I walked to and from school. They, being older, did not want their little sister tagging along (not cool) so I was relegated to walk at least six feet behind them. It was lonely back there! Until one day everything changed. I met a friend who put her hand in mine and said, "Come with me, I'll walk you home." Then, the lonely walk became a grand adventure as big as our imagination each day! The side walk turned into a raging river we had to navigate in order to save our loved ones. Or it was the aisle of the church where we would walk as radiant brides into the arms of the one to whom we would pledge our undying love. Oh, what fun we had – what a journey!

When I was thirty years old, another Friend put out His hand and said, "Come with Me, and I'll walk you home." His name is Jesus. I accepted His hand and we've been journeying together ever since. He's walking me to my eternal home – heaven.

Journeying with Jesus is God walking us to our eternal home: heaven. He reaches out His hand in invitation, and when we put our hand in His, the journey begins. He walks with us and talks with us through His Word, by His Spirit, and leads us safely "home."

Since He speaks to us and reveals Himself (His character and attributes, His will and His ways) to us through His Word, how delightful it is to spend time in His Word! *"Great are the works of the LORD; they are studied by all who delight in them"* (Psalm 111:3). It is in His Word we find His precious promises of eternity, so we can walk hand-in-hand with Him in peace and enjoy the journey.

Old Testament Scripture:

1. Let's study God's delightful Word by looking at some of the promises He's given to His children. What promises do you see in the following verses?

Psalm 37:23-24

Psalm 103:8

Isaiah 46:4

New Testament Scripture

John 3:16

John 6:37, 47

Romans 8:38-39

II Corinthians 3:18

Philippians 1:6

Philippians 2:13

Colossians 3:4

I Thessalonians 5:23-24

2. Which promise means the most to you today and why?

3. Please read Psalm 111:2. Based on this verse, why is it so delightful to study God's Word (as the theme verse of our book states)?

4. Is it delightful to you personally to study His Word – why or why not?

5. What struggles can keep studying His Word from being a delight?

6. What things can you change so studying God's Word becomes a delight for you?

 Walking with Others

Isn't knowing the Word of God wonderful? Don't these promises fill your mind with thoughts of eternity and the Person of Eternity? This is the reason we are engaging in Bible study. I want to delight in studying His Word with you, to enjoy "the sights" with you as you are *journeying with Jesus,* living with eternity in mind.

Walking In Prayer

One of God's precious promises to His children is to hear and answer when we pray (see 1 John 5:14-15), always answering by doing what is right and best. Won't you spend some time now, talking over the promises you've just studied with Him? And, as you are praying, ask Him to fill and continue to fill your heart with delight as you study His Word.

Walking in the Psalms

Meditate on Psalm 103. Make a list of all God's benefits for you and all you learn about Him. You will surely say along with the psalmist, "Bless the Lord, o my soul; and all that is within me, bless His holy name." (Bless means to speak well of – to praise.)

 ## Walking in Wonder

Write out your "I wonder" questions for class discussion.

Walking Through Today: Journaling the Journey

_____

_____

_____

_____

_____

_____

_____

_____

_____

_____

_____

_____

_____

_____

_____

_____

_____

_____

_____

_____

_____

_____

Walking Through Today: Journaling the Journey   Date:_____

Week Two

The Eternal Plan – Your Salvation

Day One   Choosing the Path

Day Two   The Call

Day Three   Change of Scenery

Day Four   Created Anew

Day Five   Committed to Christ

Choosing the Path

But the path of the righteous is like the light of dawn,
That shines brighter and brighter until the full day.
The way of the wicked is like darkness;
They do not know over what they stumble.
Proverbs 4:18-19

Walking with Him through the Word

"Two roads diverged in a wood, and I—
I took the one less traveled by,
And that has made all the difference."

This poem by Robert Frost has always been a favorite of mine. These lines come to mind often as I read the Bible. In the journey called life, though each person's journey is unique, there are really only two roads or paths. Often we are told there are many roads that will all, eventually, lead home. This is not true. The Bible tells us there are only two paths, and they each have distinctly different destinations.

1. Look up the following verses and describe the two paths or roads in the space provided. Then list what you discover on the chart at the end of today's lesson.

("Charting" is an excellent Bible study tool. To chart a passage simply means categorizing information by making lists. As you do this, you gather a body of information from the Word into one place. This gives you a more thorough picture of the subject.)

Old Testament Scripture:

Job 24:13

Proverbs 4:14

Proverbs 4:18-19

Proverbs 8:20

Proverbs 12:28

New Testament Scripture:

Matthew 7:24-27

2. Look up the following verses to further note the destinations of each path. Place what you learn on your chart.

Old Testament Scripture:

Psalm 1:6

Proverbs 14:11-12

New Testament Scripture:

Matthew 7:13–14

John 3:16

John 3:36

Romans 6:23

Optional: Read Proverbs 2. Add to your chart what you discover.

3. Proverbs 14:12 tells us, *"There is a way which seems right to a man, But its end is the way of death."* Looking at the chart you have just made, which path would that be?

Which path would you like to be on and why?

<u>Which path are you on?</u>

<u>How do you know?</u>

4. <u>How has today's study spoken to your heart?</u> <u>What has God said to you through His word?</u>

 ## Walking with Others

God's path is through Christ Jesus and leads to eternal life. Man's path is through man's philosophies and ideas and leads to eternal destruction and separation from God forever. The choice is yours. Each person chooses the path he or she will take. You either choose to *journey with Jesus,* or you choose to stay on the other path. Jesus Himself explained "You can enter God's Kingdom only through the narrow gate. The highway *[road or path]* to hell is broad, and its gate is wide for the many who choose the easy way. But the gateway to life is small, and the road is narrow, and only a few ever find it" (Matthew 7:13-14). Jesus gets explicit in John 14:6, "I am the way, the truth, and the life. No one comes to the Father except by Me."

If you chose the path to *journey with Jesus,* you are now on the sure path of eternal life and your destination is heaven, your true home. And the path leading there is a spectacular journey! It has been called, "the great adventure of knowing God."

Walking in Prayer

As you are *journeying with Jesus* right now, stop to talk with Him about what you have just studied. Through His Word, He has been speaking to you, now it's your opportunity to respond.

Walking in the Psalms

Please read and ponder Psalm 1 today. How is the blessed man characterized and what path has he chosen? How does he journey on this path? What are the results? May I encourage you to memorize this psalm? You can do it and you will be blessed!

 ## Walking in Wonder

Do you have any questions? Anything you are wondering about? Write them down, so we can find the answers together.

Verse	Path of Righteousness		Verse	Path of Unrighteousness

Walking Through Today: Journaling the Journey

_____

_____

_____

_____

_____

_____

_____

_____

_____

_____

_____

_____

_____

_____

_____

_____

_____

_____

_____

_____

_____

_____

_____

_____

_____

_____

_____

_____

_____

_____

_____

_____

_____

_____

_____

_____

_____

_____

_____

_____

_____

_____

_____

_____

_____

Walking Through Today: Journaling the Journey

Date:_____

Walking Through Today: Journaling the Journey

The Call

"For the promise is for you and your children and for all who are far off,
as many as the Lord our God will call to Himself."
Act 2:39

 ## Walking with Him through the Word

> Softly and tenderly Jesus is calling,
> Calling for you and for me.
> See on the portals He's waiting and watching
> Watching for you and for me.

This beautiful hymn by Will L. Thompson has been sung by the saints of God through the ages, as a testimony of faith to the One Who called us to salvation. We know *journeying with Jesus* is a choice we make. But how do we make it? What even brings us to the point in our lives to choose?

Today let's look at some passages of Scripture and note what they say about God's calling and choosing you.

New Testament Scripture:

1. According to Luke 5:31-32, who did Jesus call to choose His path?

2. Read Romans 3:23 and note who would fall under the category of "sinners."

3. Please read John 3:7,16, and 36. What did Jesus say you must do in verse 7?

How do we answer this call to be born again and what is the result (verse 16)?

What is the result if you do not answer His call (verse 36)?

4. According to John 6:44, Who puts the desire in our hearts to answer Christ's call?

What is Christ's promise to all who answer His call?

5. According to Acts 2:39 for whom is the promise given?

6. Please read Romans 1:6. According to this verse, how are believers defined?

7. Read II Thessalonians 2:14. How are we called and what is the result?

8. Read II Timothy 1:9. According to what were you called and when?

This is a long lesson.
Thank you for working so hard to know God's Word!
Can you keep going? Just a couple more verses.

9. Please read Romans 8:28-30. Why did God call you?

10. According to Romans 10:9-10, 13 how do you answer the call and what is the result?

11. According to all you have seen today, what must you do in order to become a child of God?

Have you answered the call?

12. <u>What does it mean to you that you are personally chosen by God to be His child?</u>

13. <u>What does it mean to you that He calls you and assures you that you will gain the glory of Christ, will be raised up, and will have eternal life?</u>

 Walking with Others

What a plan! Before the world was ever created God chose you to belong to Him. He planned for your salvation to be secured by His Son, Jesus Christ. Your responsibility is to respond to His call. And when you do, you discover He had already chosen you to be conformed to the image of His Son and to be a child of God; and He already sees you as you will someday be – glorified like Christ. Your salvation is secure because of the One who called us. He paid the price to secure it. You are on the path of faith that surely leads to eternal life.

Walking In Prayer

Take time now to meditate on what you've learned today. Write a prayer of thanksgiving to your Father and your Savior for the perfect plan of redemption. (To redeem means to buy back. Jesus Christ bought you back, with His blood, out of the slave market of sin and death. That is redemption.)

Walking in the Psalms

Read aloud Psalm 150 (reading aloud reinforces truth). Then write out your praises to the Lord for His calling and choosing you!

 ## Walking in Wonder

Do you have any questions from today's study? Don't forget to jot them down here.

Walking Through Today: Journaling the Journey

_____

_____

_____

_____

_____

_____

_____

_____

_____

_____

_____

_____

_____

_____

_____

_____

_____

_____

_____

_____

Walking Through Today: Journaling the Journey   Date:_____

Change of Scenery

"Therefore repent and return, so that your sins may be wiped away,
in order that times of refreshing may come from the presence of the Lord;
Act 3:19

 ## Walking in Him through the Word

Aren't vacations fun? You get to enjoy a change of scenery. There's always so much to see and do that is different and exciting. What will choosing God's path - answering yes to His call - mean to you personally? A change of scenery. Why? Because repentance is involved.

Repentance means "to turn around, to turn oneself," (Zodhiates) "to change one's mind or purpose, to change one's opinion. A change of mind on reflection — includes not only changing one's attitude toward and opinion of sin but also that of forsaking it." (Kenneth Wuest)

Let's look at the following verses and note what you learn about repentance.

Old Testament Scriptures:

1. Please read 2 Kings 17:13. What specific action were the Israelites to do?

This action is called repentance (see the above definition).

2. According to Proverbs 28:13 what is the result of repentance?

3. Write out Isaiah 55:6-7 in the space below and underline the key points you see about repentance?

4. Read Malachi 3:7. What will the Lord do if you repent?

New Testament Scriptures:

5. According to Matthew 4:17, Jesus' first recorded sermon, what did Jesus clearly preach and why?

Now God rules in believers' hearts. But some day He will return to rule and reign forever.

6. What was Jesus' apostles' message according to the following verses?

Mark 6:12

Luke 24:47

Acts 3:19

Acts 17:30

Romans 2:4

II Corinthians 7:9-11

7. <u>According to II Timothy 2:24-25 how is this message of repentance to be given?</u>

Just as the Spirit led you to hear the call of salvation, the Spirit also leads you to repentance. Salvation is all a work of God. He chose you, called you, and led you to repentance.

~~~~~~~~~~~~~~~~~~~~

[Note: Initial repentance leads you to and is a part of salvation. From that point on, repentance becomes part of the lifestyle of the Christian. As you are *journeying with Jesus*, you will sometimes sin and will need to confess that sin in repentance. God promises the believer in 1 John 1:9, *But if we confess our sins to him, he is faithful and just to forgive us our sins and to cleanse us from all wickedness.* Repentance leads to restoration as you once again enjoy fellowship with Christ – no barrier of sin to interfere.]

Walking with Others

Repentance is inherent in the gospel message itself. Through the gospel message, you realize you've been going your own way and not God's. You need the salvation offered by God through Christ's death, burial, and resurrection. When you hear this truth and receive it as the truth, it causes you to change your mind and turn to walk in God's way instead of your own. And what is the result? You'll enjoy a change of scenery! You've chosen the path of God in answer to His call. And if you are on His path but have fallen into sin, confess in repentance, and He will cleanse you and off you'll go on your journey with Him.

Let's see what Oswald Chambers says about repentance:

~~~~~~~~~~~~~~~~~~~~~~~~~~~~~~~~~~~~~~

My conviction of sin is best portrayed in the words:

> My sins, my sins, my Saviour,
> How sad on Thee they fell.

Conviction of sin is one of the rarest things that ever strikes a man. It is the threshold of an understanding of God. Jesus Christ said that when the Holy Spirit came He would convict of sin, and when the Holy Spirit rouses a man's conscience and brings him into the presence of God, it is not his relationship with men that bothers him, but his relationship with God – "against Thee, Thee only, have I sinned, and done this evil in Thy sight." The marvels of conviction of sin, forgiveness, and holiness are so interwoven that it is only the forgiven man who is the holy man, he proves he is forgiven by being the opposite to what he was, by God's grace. Repentance always brings a man to this point: I have sinned. The surest sign that God is at work is when a man says that and means it. Anything less than this is a remorse for having made blunders, the reflex action of disgust at himself.

The entrance into the Kingdom is through the panging pains of repentance crashing into a man's respectable goodness; then the Holy Ghost, Who produces these agonies, begins the formation of the Son of God in the life. The new life will manifest itself in conscious repentance and unconscious holiness, never the other way about. The bedrock of Christianity is repentance. Strictly speaking, a man cannot repent when he chooses; repentance is a gift of God. If ever you cease to know the virtue of repentance, you are in darkness. Examine yourself and see if you have forgotten how to be sorry.

Oswald Chambers in *My Utmost for His Highest*[5]

Walking in Prayer

Read Psalm 51 please. Is God calling you to repent – either initially to receive salvation or for a particular sin committed as a saved believer? Use this psalm to help you pray. Then, turn to Psalm 32 and rejoice, as David did, in a prayer of thanksgiving for restoration given from the Father. Record your prayer here or in your journal.

Walking in the Psalms

Please spend some more time meditating on Psalm 51 and Psalm 32. Pretend you are a reporter gathering facts about repentance. Using the journalism tool – the 5 W's and an H questions (Who, What, Where, When, Why, and How) list the facts you discover in each passage. You might ask "Who repents?" What is repentance?" "What does one repent from?" "When do you repent?" "Why do you need to repent?" "How do you repent?" "What are the results of repentance?" (You could make your own chart! Make six columns and title them with the 5 W's and an H.) For more insight into David's situation, read 2 Samuel 11:1-12:13.

 Walking in Wonder

What questions were stirred up in you today?

Walking Through Today: Journaling the Journey

_____

_____

_____

_____

_____

_____

_____

_____

_____

_____

_____

_____

_____

_____

_____

_____

_____

_____

_____

_____

_____

Walking Through Today: Journaling the Journey

Date:_____

Created Anew

*Therefore if anyone is in Christ, he is a new creature;
the old things passed away; behold, new things have come.*
II Corinthians 5:17

 ## Walking with Him through the Word

We all know the metamorphosis of the butterfly. He begins life as a caterpillar, undergoes a burial in the cocoon, and is raised a butterfly. He's a completely new creation, although the same creature. When we choose the path of God, answer the call of Christ in repentance, resulting in a change of scenery: this is called salvation. Like the caterpillar to the butterfly, you are created anew. And, like the butterfly, who goes from crawling to flying, you can now live in a new way, *journeying with Jesus.*

New Testament Scriptures:

You have a new reality

1. According to the following verses, what is your new reality?

John 5:24

Galatians 2:20

2. <u>Read Ephesians 2:1-5</u>.   <u>What were you before you were saved and what did God give you?</u>

<u>You have a new citizenship</u>

3. <u>What do the following verses tell you about your new citizenship?</u> <u>Where is it?</u>

<u>Philippians 3:20</u>

<u>Colossians 1:13</u>

<u>You have a new way of walking - of living life</u>

4. <u>You can now live a new life, set free from what according to Romans 6:4-7?</u>

5. <u>Look up the following verses and note how you are to walk in your new life</u>.

<u>Ephesians 4:1-2</u>

Ephesians 5:2

Colossians 2:6-7

You have a new work to do

6. From the following verses, what is your new work?

II Corinthians 5:18-20

Ephesians 2:10

You have a new purpose

7. According to the following verses, what is your new purpose?

Matthew 5:16

Matthew 22:37-39

I Corinthians 6:20

I John 5:20

Revelation 3:20

8.   What has meant the most to you today as you have studied these truths concerning "the new you?"

What are the changes you need to make in your life, so you are living according to your new purpose?

9. Read II Corinthians 5:17 and write out this magnificent truth word for word in the space below.

Are you a new creation in Christ? This is called salvation. The circumstance surrounding your salvation is often called your "salvation experience." Can you describe your salvation experience? The telling of your salvation experience is called your "testimony." God uses our testimonies to draw others to Him. It's good to be able to "share your testimony" of the marvelous, saving work of Jesus Christ.

Using the butterfly analogy, write briefly of your life as a caterpillar, the cocooning process, and re-birth as a butterfly – i.e. your testimony here:

Walking with Others
Salvation is the wonderful gift that begins your personal *journey with Jesus.* You are a new creation and can grow in deep, intimate relationship with God your Father. It can be a heart-to-Heart relationship that goes beyond mere head knowledge. You now have a new purpose for life – to bring glory to God and a new way of walking (living) in obedience to the Lord. Created anew! What a life!

~~~~~~

I am a New Creation

I am a new creation
No more in condemnation
Here in the grace of God I stand.

Chorus:
And I will praise You, Lord
Yes, I'll praise You, Lord
I will sing of all that You have done.

My heart is overflowing
My love just keeps on growing
Here in the grace of God I stand.

Dave Bilbrough [6]

Walking in Prayer

Spend some time in prayer, thanking God for your new life in Christ. You might read and meditate on the prayer in Colossians 1:9-14. How can you pray concerning your new life according to these verses (for example: pray He will fill you with the knowledge of His will).

Walking in the Psalms

Please meditate on Psalm 138 today. What do you learn about your relationship with the Lord as His new creation?

 ## Walking in Wonder

I wonder…

Walking Through Today: Journaling the Journey

_____

_____

_____

_____

_____

_____

_____

_____

_____

_____

_____

_____

_____

_____

_____

_____

_____

_____

_____

_____

Walking Through Today: Journaling the Journey   Date:_____

Committed to Christ

...for I know whom I have believed and I am convinced
that He is able to guard what I have entrusted to Him until that day.
II Timothy 1:12b

 ## Walking with Him through the Word

You have surely noticed in choosing the path, God chose you first – before the foundation of the world. In answering the call, you discovered He gave you ears to hear His voice and spiritual eyes to see you were going the wrong way, He put repentance in your heart, and certainly, He's the One who created you anew. Your salvation is all the work of God, given to you as a gift. This is called _grace_. Grace is the special, unearned, unmerited **favor** of God to save you, keep you, change you, and walk you safely home to heaven.

Such a treasured gift begets a response. It calls for a life commitment to your Lord and Savior, Jesus Christ.

New Testament Scripture:

1. <u>As a reminder, read Ephesians 2:8-9. How are you saved? Who saved you? Did you have to earn it in any way? Why or why not?</u>

2. <u>Read Romans 5:1-2. Since you are saved, where do you now stand?</u>

<u>In what do you exalt?</u>

3. <u>What is the commitment of a believer?</u> <u>Read the following verses and note what you see as your commitment</u>.

<u>Matthew 4:10 (a quote of Deuteronomy 6:13)</u>

<u>Matthew 22:37-39</u>

<u>Luke 9:23-24</u>

4. <u>Now, from the following verses, what are the results of your commitment?</u>

<u>Matthew 11:28-30</u>

<u>John 14: 1-3, 21-23</u>

Romans 8:28-30

II Peter 1:2-4

Jude verse24

Revelation 21:1-7

Walking with Others

The commitment to God in response to His gift of grace is the commitment to love! <u>We are committed to walk in His path of love.</u> He loved us so much He sent His Son to die for our sins, so we could walk with Him, in love, now and for eternity. And He has promised and given us everything we need now to live godly lives – loving Him and loving others – as He works in us to transform our lives so we reflect our Savior and Lord, Jesus Christ. And He has promised to keep that which we have committed to Him – our hearts – until the day we see Him face-to-Face, safely at home in heaven. Oh, what grace! Oh, what love! Oh, what a Savior!

~~~~~~

I KNOW WHOM I HAVE BELIEVED

I know not why God's wondrous grace To me He has made known,
Nor why, unworthy, Christ in love, Redeemed me as His own.

(chorus)
But I know whom I have believed, and am persuaded that He is able
To keep that which I've committed, Unto Him against that day.

I know not how this saving faith To me He did impart.
Nor how believing in His word Wrought peace within my heart.

I know not how the Spirit moves, Convincing men of sin,
Revealing Jesus through the word, Creating faith in Him.

I know not when my Lord may come, At night or noon-day fair,
Nor if I walk the vale with Him, Or meet Him in the air.

Daniel Whittle [7]

Walking in Prayer

How have you responded to His commitment to you? What do you want to give to Him in thanksgiving for all He's given you? Open your heart to Him now in worship and prayer.

Walking in the Psalms

Read and meditate today on Psalm 65. Focusing on verse 4, how do you see God's loving action toward you personally? What is your commitment and response to Him?

 Walking in Wonder

Any Questions?

Walking Through Today: Journaling the Journey

_____

_____

_____

_____

_____

_____

_____

_____

_____

_____

_____

_____

_____

_____

_____

_____

_____

_____

_____

_____

_____

_____

_____

_____

_____

_____

_____

_____

_____

_____

_____

_____

_____

_____

_____

_____

_____

_____

_____

_____

_____

_____

_____

_____

_____

_____

Walking Through Today: Journaling the Journey   Date:_____

Walking Through Today: Journaling the Journey

Provisions for the Journey

Week Three	The Holy Spirit
Week Four	The Word of God
Week Five	Prayer
Week Six	The Body of Christ

Week Three

The Holy Spirit

Day One   Secured by the Holy Spirit

Day Two   Convicted and Convinced by the Spirit

Day Three Indwelt and Filled by the Spirit

Day Four   Fruit Produced by the Spirit

Day Five   Gifted by the Spirit

Secured by the Holy Spirit

In Him, you also, after listening to the message of truth,
the gospel of your salvation--having also believed,
you were sealed in Him with the Holy Spirit of promise
Ephesians 1:13

 ## Walking With Him through the Word

Being directionally impaired can be hazardous to your health. You can get off the trail and find yourself in a real dilemma. Even an astute hiker can find himself in trouble. Recently some friends went on a short hike. Since it was so short they had no provisions with them. After reaching their destination one friend decided to head back down the trail earlier than his other friends. Easy right? Just follow the trail. What could go wrong? Twenty minutes later, he realized he was no longer on the trail nor was the trail in sight. After much wandering through dangerous ground he made his way back to the trailhead where his friends were anxiously waiting.

Spiritually, it is the same. It is easy to get off the trail while journeying (not the path of salvation, that's secure, but the path of obedience). If you let go of your Companion's hand, you can find yourself feeling alone, in danger, frightened.... God knows this, so He has given us provisions for our journey – a compass, a guidebook, a walkie-talkie, and friends to help us on the way. For the next four weeks let's examine our provisions, identify them, their purpose, and learn how to effectively use them (they won't do us any good unless we know and use them).

The first provision God has given us is a compass. What does a compass do? It gives direction. Our spiritual compass is God, the Holy Spirit. In week 1, day 3, we noted the Holy Spirit is the Person of Eternity (One of the Trinity). Let's begin by looking at Who He is according to Scripture.

Old Testament Scriptures:

1. Read Genesis 1:2. Who was there at creation?

2. Read 1 Samuel 10:6 (Samuel was anointing Saul to be the first King of Israel) and 1 Samuel 16:13. Who came upon both Saul and David?

In the Old Testament you will notice the Holy Spirit 'came upon' people like Saul and David for the purpose of service. He directed them to do God's will much like a compass directs and points the way.

3. Now read 1 Samuel 16:14. What did the Spirit do?

4. Please read Ezekiel 36:26-27. What does God promise He will do in these verses?

God promises to put His Spirit within the believer. We see Him fulfill this promise in the New Testament.

New Testament Scriptures:

5. Read John 14:16-17. Who did Jesus promise to send? What will he do? How long will He stay?

6. According to Romans 8:16 what does the Spirit's Presence do?

7. Read Ephesians 1:13-14. To whom does the Holy Spirit come and when?

According to these verses, what three reasons does Paul give as to why the Holy Spirit is given to us?

8. How does knowing you are forever indwelt by the Holy Spirit of God comfort you?

9. <u>In your walk today, how will the Holy Spirit, like a compass, guide you?</u>

 ## Walking With Others

These are the facts: the Holy Spirit is the Person of Eternity who energized the creation of the heavens and the earth – time, space, and matter – the creation of <u>you</u>. He is eternal – from eternity past to eternity future. He is God.

In the Old Testament the Holy Spirit would come into someone's life for service. He might also leave when service was finished. So He would come and go. In the New Testament Jesus promised to send the Holy Spirit to live within the believer forever – never to leave. He is the witness within your hearts that you are God's very own child and will enjoy the inheritance of your Father with Christ. All His promises He made are yours, now and forever. As you study, you will see not only are you indwelt by the Holy Spirit for service, as some were in the Old Testament, but you are also indwelt for sanctification – transforming you from the inside out, making you like Jesus. What a gracious God!

Walking In Prayer

Spend some time in prayer thanking God for this wonderful gift of His indwelling Holy Spirit who will never leave us nor forsake us. Thank Him for what His indwelling Spirit means to you.

Walking In the Psalms

Spend some time enjoying Psalm 16, meditating on the words. What do you notice in this Psalm that corresponds with what you studied today?

 Walking in Wonder

Please note any questions you might have today. If they are not answered in the next four days' study, we want to be sure to answer them in class.

Walking Through Today: Journaling the Journey

_____

_____

_____

_____

_____

_____

_____

_____

_____

_____

_____

_____

_____

_____

_____

_____

_____

_____

_____

_____

_____

Walking Through Today: Journaling the Journey   Date:_____

Convicted and Convinced by the Spirit

*"And He, when He comes, will convict the world
concerning sin and righteousness and judgment*
John 16:8

 ## Walking With Him through the Word

As a compass has the distinct purpose of giving direction, so the Holy Spirit has a distinct purpose. Today, let's answer the questions: what is the reason the Spirit was sent by Christ to indwell believers, what does He do, and how does He do it?

New Testament Scriptures:

1. Read John 16:14. What is the Holy Spirit's encompassing purpose?

According to this verse, how does He do this?

2. Read John 16:8-11 and list what the Holy Spirit does and why.

What Holy Spirit Does	Why?

3. <u>How is the indwelling Holy Spirit bringing glory to Christ in your life today?</u>

 ## Walking With Others

Jesus, knowing He was going back to heaven, His rightful place, promised God would send the Holy Spirit to indwell all true believers. He, the Holy Spirit, would glorify Christ. He, like a compass, would direct people to Christ. He would shine the spotlight on the Lord Jesus Christ who is the Way, the Truth, and the Life (see John 14:6); for Christ had done the all-sufficient work of salvation. The Word of God, 2 Peter 1:21 tells us, was given to godly men moved by the Holy Spirit. They wrote down the Word of God for us. Now the indwelling Holy Spirit directs us to the Word and illuminates it to our understanding so we can see, know, and follow Christ Jesus. Wow!

Why does the Holy Spirit point to and glorify Jesus by convicting the people of their unbelief? The unbelievers need to be convicted of unbelief so they will see their need to believe in Christ and be forgiven of all their sins. (As the Holy Spirit indwells believers and their lives are transformed into godly, holy, *journeying with* Jesus walks of belief, unbelievers are convicted of their own sin of unbelief and their need to believe.)

How does the Holy Spirit glorify Christ by convicting the world of God's righteousness? He points to the only One who is righteous – right with God, perfectly holy, sinless – that's Jesus Christ. How do you know He was righteous? Because He rose from the dead and He ascended to the Father. The Holy Spirit points to the only One who can make you righteous.

And, how does this Holy Spirit convict the world of judgment? When Jesus came explaining God's love by His life, death, and resurrection, Satan's lie was revealed and his power permanently crushed. Satan was judged for his lies that held the world in his grasp, but the Holy Spirit points to the Life-Giver, Jesus Christ, Who conquered death so you can come from death to life – move from the kingdom of darkness to the Kingdom of Light.

Did you notice that 'He convicts you to convince you of Jesus' – of His love, His care, His salvation, the inheritance of heaven and of the joy of living for Him? He always glorifies your Lord so you will see His glory, desire to come to Him, and live for His glory alone.

Walking In Prayer

Another awesome thing the Holy Spirit does is direct our prayers. Romans 8:26 says "and the Holy Spirit helps us in our weakness. For example, we don't know what God wants us to pray for. But the Holy Spirit prays for us with groanings that cannot be expressed in words" (NLT). Isn't this good news? As you pray for certain people's situations and circumstances, you pray the generalities and at the same time, the Holy Spirit also prays, pointing out the particulars – not to you, but to the Father.

As God's own, how is the Lord convincing or convicting you today? How does He want you to glorify the Lord today? Write out your prayer, knowing the Holy Spirit is praying for you in the particulars.

Walking In the Psalms

Meditate on Psalm 139. List all the things the Psalmist is convicted and convinced of and how he then prays.

 ## Walking in Wonder

Any questions?

👣 Walking Through Today: Journaling the Journey

_____

_____

_____

_____

_____

_____

_____

_____

_____

_____

_____

_____

_____

_____

_____

_____

_____

_____

_____

_____

_____

_____

_____

_____

_____

_____

_____

_____

_____

_____

_____

_____

_____

_____

_____

_____

_____

_____

_____

_____

_____

_____

Walking Through Today: Journaling the Journey   Date:_____

Indwelt and Filled by the Spirit

*And the disciples were continually filled with joy
and with the Holy Spirit.*
Act 13:52

Walking with Him through the Word

Journeying with Jesus is a life-walk, with the indwelling Holy Spirit directing us to glorify the Lord Jesus Christ. Today we want to look at how we are to do that.

New Testament Scripture:
1. Read and write out in the space below Galatians 5:25.

According to this verse, what are we to do?

2. What are we told to do in Ephesians 5:18.?

3. Please read John 16:13. How is the Holy Spirit going to lead us as He fills us?

4. In Ephesians 4:29-30, what are we instructed 'not' to do?

5. According to 1 Thessalonians 5:19, what are we not to do?

6. What are some ways you can grieve or quench the Spirit?

 ## Walking with Others

The word 'filled' means to be 'empowered or controlled by.' So Ephesians 5:18 confirms Galatians 5:22 where you are told to walk in the Spirit or be led by the Spirit. You are to follow the Spirit's leading yielding to His control to empower you to do so. The grammatical construction in the original language tells you this is to be your ongoing lifestyle. The Holy Spirit is God – the Person of Eternity – sent to indwell you and to lead you into all truth. Like a compass, He points you to a lifestyle of *journeying with Jesus.*

As a Christian, you are 'indwelt' by the Holy Spirit **forever** and can never 'lose' Him. But, being 'filled' by the Spirit is a choice. If you choose not to be filled with the Spirit, it doesn't mean you are less 'indwelt,' it just means that you are not choosing to surrender to His control and empowerment. And what a loss that would be for your life. You would not be honoring the One who loves you, died and rose again for you, and now indwells you to guide your life in the good, right way.

When you choose to wander off the path of obedience, ignoring your Compass Point, you grieve Him and stifle His work in your life. Believers still have free-will and can choose to refuse to go the way He directs, not bringing glory to Christ. Doesn't it break your heart to know you can grieve your Lord?

The good news is because the Spirit does indwell you, you are totally empowered to yield in surrender to His leading and guiding your life. It's your choice. Just as you received Christ by faith at salvation, now by faith (the same faith) you choose to walk with Him and in Him. As He guides you into all truth – found in His Word – you simply obey and trust Him to be faithful to His Word. You hold tightly to His hand and trust Him to walk you all the way home.

Walking in Prayer

Are you glorifying Christ by walking in the Spirit, controlled and empowered by Him? Are you in any way grieving Him or stifling His work? Spend some time in prayer examining yourself before God.

Walking in the Psalms

Using Psalm 115, ponder the greatness of your God. According to verse 9, who is He to you and what does that mean to you?

 Walking in Wonder

I wonder . . .

Walking Through Today: Journaling the Journey

_____

_____

_____

_____

_____

_____

_____

_____

_____

_____

_____

_____

_____

_____

_____

_____

_____

_____

_____

_____

_____

Walking Through Today: Journaling the Journey   Date:_____

Fruit Produced by the Spirit

"I am the vine, you are the branches;
he who abides in Me and I in him
he bears much fruit,
for apart from Me you can do nothing.
John 15:5

 ## Walking with Him through the Word

Journeying with Jesus is a Spirit led walk of faith, trusting God each step of the way. And as you walk in the Spirit – in faith – there are wonderful results in your life. The Word describes it as 'fruit.' The Holy Spirit produces fruit – a harvest of fruit (results) in your life as you determine, by faith, to walk where the Compass points, **to glorify Christ** with your lives.

New Testament Scripture:

1. According to John 4:36 how does Jesus describe the fruit?

2. Read Romans 6:22. What is the benefit (fruit) you see in your life as one who is a slave of God *journeying with Jesus*?

3. Read Romans 15:26-28 please. What is the fruit you see in these verses?

4. Please read Ephesians 5:9 and note how the fruit described.

5. <u>Examine Colossians 1:8-10. According to verse 8, what fruit has the Holy Spirit given you?</u>

<u>What is the prayer for those given this special supernatural love for others (see verse 9)?</u>

<u>According to verse 10, what would be the result of this prayer?</u>

<u>How does the Holy Spirit giving you love for others and your life producing every kind of good fruit, fit together?</u>

6. <u>According to Hebrews 13:15 how is fruit described?</u>

7. <u>Turn to Galatians 5:22-23a</u>. <u>Here you find what seems to be a list of fruits or results</u>. <u>Actually it is only one fruit that is followed by aspects of the fruit</u>. <u>The fruit is 'love.'</u> <u>How is this love described?</u>

<u>Who produces this fruit?</u>

8. <u>Now, using all your answers from all the verses you have looked at, make a list of the fruit (the results) the Holy Spirit produces in the life of a believer as the believer walks by faith in Christ.</u>

Wow! We will look like our Lord Jesus Christ.

I know this is a long study. Thank you for your hard work.
Isn't it worth it to know the truths of God?

9. <u>Finally, according to John 15:5, how does the Holy Spirit produce this fruit in your life?</u>

<u>What are some practical ways you can "abide in Christ?"</u>

 ## Walking with Others

Here is the picture: fruit is produced on a vine. As the nutrients come up from the roots through the trunk into the branch, so the branch, being healthy, remains on the vine. The branch does not have to struggle to produce fruit. You, as a believer, do not have to struggle and fret or work to produce the fruit of the Spirit. You simply abide – remain in close personal fellowship with Christ – *journeying with Jesus* in faith, trusting and obeying His good word to you.

As you abide, the Holy Spirit produces in your heart and life, the fruit (results) you've just studied. How fruitful will you be? That depends on how closely you choose to abide. Don't let go of Christ's hand. Don't wander away. Walk in the Spirit. Delight yourself in Him. Obey Him. Love Him. Love others. Be a person of prayer and of the Word and you will bear much fruit. You will be Christlike, and God will use you to draw others to Himself.

Walking in Prayer

Are you abiding in Christ – *journeying* closely *with Jesus*? If you are, John 15:7 assures you that you may ask for anything you want and it will be granted. When you abide in Christ, He conforms your desires to His will. You will, then, pray only for those things that are pleasing to Him. For what do you wish to pray today?

Walking in the Psalms

Meditate on Psalm 1. What does the person do in verses one and two that depicts abiding? What are the results in this person's life in verse three? According to verse 6 how does God comfort this person? Are you this person?

Isn't it exciting to see that abiding with the Lord (verses 1 and 2) produces such wonderful fruit (verse 3).

 Walking in Wonder

Any questions?

Walking Through Today: Journaling the Journey

_____

_____

_____

_____

_____

_____

_____

_____

_____

_____

_____

_____

_____

_____

_____

_____

_____

_____

_____

_____

_____

_____

_____

Walking Through Today: Journaling the Journey   Date:_____

Gifted by the Spirit

Whoever speaks, is to do so as one who is speaking the utterances of God;
whoever serves is to do so as one who is serving by the strength which God supplies;
so that in all things God may be glorified through Jesus Christ,
to whom belongs the glory and dominion forever and ever. Amen.
1 Peter 4:11

 ## Walking with Him through the Word

By now you have certainly realized God is the Giver of gifts. He gifted you with salvation – eternal life, and the indwelling Spirit as the Compass to direct your life to glorify Christ and in doing so, make you Christlike. Well, there is even more. He has also blessed His own with "giftedness." Giftedness is the supernatural ability given to believers by the Holy Spirit to bless one another in the body of Christ, the church.

Although you will be studying this more later, let's gather some basic facts about giftedness now. Although the entire New Testament is filled with exhortations to each Christian to use their giftedness to love and serve one another, there are four places in the Word of God where the gifts are particularly emphasized. These four places are easy to remember: Romans 12; 1 Corinthians 12 (two "12's"); Ephesians 4 and 1 Peter 4 (two "4's").

Today, let's begin with the last passage and work our way forward.

I want to thank you in advance for your labor of love
as you toil over the Word of God. Your labor will not be in vain.

New Testament Scripture

1. Read 1 Peter 4:10. What are we responsible to do with the gifts He has given us?

2. What two categories of gifts are given in 1 Peter 4:11?

What does this verse say is our particular responsibility with these giftings?

Speaking Gifts:

Serving Gifts:

And, according to this verse, what is the goal of the Holy Spirit's empowerment for using your gift(s)?

Once again the Holy Spirit is your Compass pointing to Christ to glorify Him. It is all about Him and not about you. This keeps pride from your life.

3. Moving to the next passage, please read Ephesians 4:11-16. According to verse 11 to whom are these gifts given?

In what category (speaking or serving) do these specific gifts fall?

Why were these particular gifts given according to verse 12?

As each one uses their giftedness what will be the result (verse 13)?

Verses 14 and 15 show the contrast between immature and mature Christians. What is the difference?

Immature	Mature

How does verse 16 summarize how God uses our giftedness?

4. Please read 1 Corinthians 12:4-31 in order to answer the following questions (I know it's a long passage but we're just looking for the basics -- *"Keep up the good work!"*) In verses 4-6 what things are different and what's the same?

Different/Varieties of	Same

According to verse 7 what is the purpose of spiritual gifts?

Also, according to verse 7, to whom are the spiritual gifts given?

What important truth is emphasized in verse 11?

In verses 12-26, what analogy is used to explain spiritual giftedness?

According to the questions asked in verses 29 and 30, does every believer have the same gifts or any one believer have all the gifts?

You are doing great – what a spiritual workout!

5. Finally, read Romans 12:3-8 please. According to verse 3, what warning is given and what are we to do?

Warning	What Are We to Do?

God loves the body of believers (His church). And He's not only given each one of you the faith to believe, and the privilege of having an intimate relationship with Him, but also the ability to serve Him using your particular spiritual gift(s).

Have you noticed you've been using
your Bible study tool of charting in this lesson?
Isn't it helpful?

<u>Keeping in mind what you learned in 1 Corinthians 12 above, look at the body analogy in this Romans passage. You will see that no one part is more important nor less vital nor less necessary than the other parts. What is the key point being made in verses 6 and 7 of Romans 12?</u>

<u>Having examined just the basics of the giftedness you have from God, what is the Holy Spirit pointing you to do?</u>

Walking with Others

Often there is an anxiousness and over-emphasis on discovering one's personal, spiritual gift(s). Sometimes there are tests presented to help you discover your spiritual gift(s). Or you are encouraged to pray for certain spiritual gifts. But here are the basics. As a believer in Christ you are indwelt and empowered by His Spirit to abide in Him and thus be fruitful. You are exhorted and commanded to 'speak' His truth and 'serve' with His love. This is the giftedness given to every believer. Just do it. And as you do, He will open the doors of opportunity to use your particular spiritual gift(s). It's His work. Remember 1 Corinthians 12 – He gives the gifts, the places of ministry, and the effects. So "speak" the Word, :"serve" with His strength and enjoy the giftedness of the Spirit.

Walking in Prayer

Speaking about and serving the Lord – your Head – what a gift! Spend some time in prayer praising God that, as His child, you have the giftedness of His Spirit. As the Apostle Paul prayed, pray for open doors to use your giftedness to glorify Him so others are helped and drawn to Him.

Walking in the Psalms

Meditate please on Psalm 100. How are you encouraged to both speak and serve the Lord?

 Walking in Wonder

You may have many questions. Be sure to list any you might have so we can be sure to cover them in class.

Walking Through Today: Journaling the Journey

_____

_____

_____

_____

_____

_____

_____

_____

_____

_____

_____

_____

_____

_____

_____

_____

_____

_____

_____

_____

_____

_____

_____

Walking Through Today: Journaling the Journey   Date:_____

Week Four

The Word of God

The Eternal Guidebook

The words of the LORD are pure words;
As silver tried in a furnace on the earth,
refined seven times
Psalm 12:6

 ## Walking with Him through the Word

My husband and I love road trips. It is one of our favorite things to do. And we are so thankful for Triple AAA. They provide great guidebooks for each state in America so we can easily arrive at our destination. Once familiar with how to use it, you discover the guidebook is a sufficient resource. Call me weird, but I read – really read – these guidebooks cover to cover. It's amazing what can be discovered in a simple guidebook, and if followed, it will lead you on the best, safest route to your desired destination.

The Lord has given you a guidebook: the Bible. This is one of His grand provisions for His children as they are *journeying with Jesus.* This Guidebook, if read and heeded, is filled with specific directions for the twists and turns of the road you travel called 'life's highway.' But this book is different from any guidebook written by man for it is God's Word, so it is perfect and complete, without error, and never gets outdated.

This week, may I point out some basic information about this Guidebook to help you use it effectively? You'll be amazed at God's perfect provision.

Like all guidebooks, the Bible tells you some things about itself, so you can know it is reliable. Let's note what it says about itself.

Old Testament Scriptures:

1. <u>Who's word is written in the Bible according to the following verses?</u>

<u>Psalm 12:6</u>

Psalm 33:4

New Testament Scriptures:

Mark 13:31

2. From the following verses, when did God's Word originate? (How is it different from every other book?)

Old Testament Scriptures:

Psalm 119:52

Psalm 119:89

New Testament Scriptures:

I Peter 1:25 (quoting Isaiah 40:8)

3. Who wrote the Bible according to the following Scriptures?

Old Testament Scriptures:

Zechariah 7:12

New Testament Scriptures:

Luke 1:70

Romans 1:1-2

II Peter 1:20-21

4. What does it mean to you to know the Bible is God's very own word written to you?

 Walking with Others

The Bible is a unique book, like no other. It says of itself it is the eternal Word of God, penned by His prophets as given to them by His Holy Spirit. God is God and cannot lie, so every word is true. That makes this Guidebook the most reliable resource you can have for *journeying* life's highway *with Jesus*. Praise the Lord!

~~~~~~

> "This [Bible] is the writing of the living God; each letter was penned with an Almighty finger; each word in it dropped from the everlasting lips; each sentence was dictated by the Holy Spirit."

> Charles Haddon Spurgeon [8]

Walking in Prayer

As you think of the gift of the wonderful provision of God's Word and the care of the Giver to provide and preserve it for you, take time to respond in prayerful thanksgiving. Why don't you write out your prayer here or on your journal pages?

Walking in the Psalms

The longest psalm written is a psalm extolling the Word of God- Psalm 119. Read and meditate on the first 4 stanzas – verses 1-32. You will notice the Word of God is referred to as the word, statutes, law, commandments, precepts, and judgments. Underline these words as you come across them and write them on the following chart. Make a list of what God is telling you about His Word. Take your time. This is a wonderful, lifetime of discovery.

Verse	Word	Qualities/Characteristics of the Word

Walking in Wonder

I wonder....

Walking Through Today: Journaling the Journey

_____

_____

_____

_____

_____

_____

_____

_____

_____

_____

_____

_____

_____

_____

_____

_____

_____

_____

_____

_____

_____

_____

_____

_____

_____

_____

_____

_____

_____

_____

_____

_____

_____

_____

_____

_____

_____

_____

_____

_____

_____

_____

_____

Walking Through Today: Journaling the Journey   Date:_____

The Wonder of the Word

Your words were found and I ate them,
And Your words became for me a joy and the delight of my heart
For I have been called by Your name, O LORD God of hosts.
Jeremiah 15:16

Walking with Him through the Word

The Bible is God's special book,
His words are written there.
And as I turn each page to look,
I handle it with care.
Author Unknown

Sitting in a circle, looking with expectant faces, my Bible Study Fellowship classes of three and four year olds would hold up their "pretend Bibles" and repeat this rhyme with me each week. They knew it was "Bible Story Time," and I was going to open my real Bible and tell them a true story, because "it's God's Word and it's always true and right."

Do you realize how special your Bible is – how true and right? Do you handle it with care, studying with delight and diligence, because it's God's very own Word to you?

New Testament Scripture:

1. <u>Write out word for word II Timothy 2:15.</u>

<u>According to this verse, what are you exhorted to do with the Word of God?</u>

2. <u>Why is it so important that you work hard to be able to correctly explain the word</u> <u>of truth? Read II Timothy 2:16-18 to help you answer.</u>

3. <u>Read Hebrews 4:12-16. List what verse 12 tells you about the Word. What makes</u> <u>it different from every other book in the world?</u>

<u>According to verse 13 to whom are you accountable for your response to the Word?</u>

<u>Who is your High Priest, the One who died for your sins (those sins that come from</u> <u>wrong heart motives)?</u>

<u>What is your privilege now as His child?</u>

The wonder of the Word is that it exposes 'heart' motives. No other book can do this. They can play with your emotions, but cannot expose your heart. Only God can do that. And only God provided the Living Word through Whom He pours out His grace and mercy upon His children as our High Priest. He offered Himself to take away our sin and lives to make intercession for you. What a wonder!

4. <u>According to Ephesians 5:26 and 27, how are God's children made holy and clean and why?</u>

5. <u>What is the most striking truth to you from all the verses you have studied today?</u>

 Walking with Others

No other book in the world is full of living power! No other book is the Word of God. It is written by the one, true, living God. The power inherent in the Word is the power of God Almighty. What a wonder! Because the Word is sharp to reveal God's perfect standard and expose even your heart motives, you are able to see yourself as a sinner who falls short of God's perfection. As you do, more and more you realize the wonder of God's plan of redemption – to send Jesus Christ to save you. His Word assures you of the truth of Who He is and what He did as your High Priest to offer His blood as **the** sacrifice for your sin. Now you can live in freedom. You can come boldly (meaning with humble assurance) before the throne of your Father to receive help when you need it most – when you are weak, have sinned, or are tempted to sin. His Word is your Guidebook to Him, the One Who ever lives to present you holy and without blame before the throne of God! Hallelujah! What a Savior! What a book!

Walking in Prayer

After our Bible Study Fellowship Bible story time, each child would have a "turn" to stand by Teacher and "read" from the Bible, repeating the week's verse. What a humbling privilege to see and hear the awe these children had for God's Word! Are you in awe? Then, take this time to offer up a prayer of praise either here or on your journal page. If you discover you are not really in awe or have lost your awe, go boldly (with humble assurance) before His throne and ask for Him to give you awe for His Word as you worship Him.

Walking in the Psalms

Continue to read and meditate on Psalm 119, focusing today on stanzas 5-8, verses 33-64. What wonders of His Word do you see in these verses? Worship Him in wonder.

Stanza 5 (verses 33-40)	Stanza 6 (verses 41-48)	Stanza 7 (verses 49-56)	Stanza 8 (verses 57-64)

Walking in Wonder

Any questions?

Walking in Wonder

Walking Through Today: Journaling the Journey

Walking Through Today: Journaling the Journey   Date:_____

The Sufficiency of the Word

How can a young man keep his way pure?
By keeping it according to Your word.
Psalm 119:9

 ## Walking with Him through the Word

My Aunt Sheila begins each day in a special way. Very early in the morning, she opens her shutters on her bedroom sliding door, grabs her coffee, plumps her pillows, settles back in bed and awaits the sunrise! She greets her heavenly Father with praise for His glorious creation, and then she reaches for His Word to get her "marching orders" for the day. She knows whatever she reads will guide her faithfully, as it is the Voice of her faithful God.

Old Testament Scriptures:

1. <u>Read Psalm 19:1-6.</u> <u>How can everyone on the face of the earth know there is a God?</u>

2. Now read verses 7-11. On the chart below, list the term used for God's Word, how it is described/defined, and its results in your life.

Verse	Term for God's Word	Description	Results

New Testament Scriptures:

3. Read II Timothy 3:16-17. Note what word is used to describe the Word of God, how it is defined, and it's results.

Verse	Term for God's Word	Description	Results

<u>How can you use these verses to evaluate each passage of Scripture you study?</u>

<u>According to verse 17, what else beside the Word of God is needed to equip and prepare you to live a life of *journeying with Jesus*?</u>

 ## Walking with Others

Isn't it incredible how sufficient the Word of God is as the Guidebook for your life? Hearing, reading, and following this perfect, trustworthy Word of the God of creation will keep you steady on the path, peaceful on the journey, and able to enjoy the scenery as you walk in Him and with Him.

~~~~~~

"Sound Bible exposition is an imperative must in the Church of the Living God. Without it no church can be a New Testament church in any strict meaning of that term. But exposition may be carried on in a way as to leave the hearers devoid of any true spiritual nourishment whatever. "For it is not mere words that nourish the soul, but God Himself, and unless and until the hearers find GOD in personal experience they are not the better for having heard the truth. The Bible is not an end in itself, but a means to bring men to an intimate and satisfying knowledge of God, that they may enter into Him, that they may delight in His presence, may taste and know the inner sweetness of God Himself in the care and center of their hearts."

A W. Tozer in *The Pursuit of God*[9]

Walking in Prayer

Spend some time praising God for revealing Himself to you both in creation and in His Word. Thank Him for the heart to believe and the desire to know Him through His wonderful Word. Ask Him give you understanding and a willingness to obey as you are made aware of instructions, reproofs, corrections, and training practices as you study this wonderful Guidebook. You might want to write out your prayer below or on your journal pages to help you reflect on what you have prayed.

Walking in the Psalms

Read and ponder stanzas 9-12, verses 65-96 of Psalm 119. Isn't it such a rich Psalm!! List the benefits of the Word in your life. Examine yourself to see if you are taking full advantage of these benefits. What changes might you need to make?

Stanza 9 (verses 65-72)	Stanza 10 (verses 73-80)	Stanza 11 (verses 81-88)	Stanza 12 (verses 89-96)

Walking in Wonder

Be sure to jot down any questions you might have as you've studied this day's lesson.

Walking in Wonder

Walking Through Today: Journaling the Journey

_____

_____

_____

_____

_____

_____

_____

_____

_____

_____

_____

_____

_____

_____

_____

_____

_____

_____

_____

_____

_____

_____

Walking Through Today: Journaling the Journey   Date:_____

 Walking Through Today: Journaling the Journey

The Simplicity of the Word

And He said to him, " 'YOU SHALL LOVE THE LORD YOUR GOD WITH ALL YOUR HEART,
AND WITH ALL YOUR SOUL, AND WITH ALL YOUR MIND.'
"This is the great and foremost commandment.
"The second is like it, 'YOU SHALL LOVE YOUR NEIGHBOR AS YOURSELF.'
Matthew 22:37-39

 ## Walking with Him through the Word

I received a Bible study reference book as a gift. It's been proclaimed to be, and I'm sure it is, a valuable study tool and asset to one's library. The only problem is there are no directions as to how to use it. There are reference columns with no corresponding verses, arrows pointing to nowhere, letters and numbers to who knows what. I am determined and will figure it all out and eventually benefit by this book, but it's not easy. (No one ever labeled me as a genius either, so that could be part of the problem.)

The Word of God can look daunting. Being all that it is and as important as each word is, since it is God's own Word to us, it could seem 'too much' to delve into – 'too much' to try to grasp, understand, and follow. If you're thinking this, you are not alone. Believers through the ages have had the same concern. God knew this – He is God, after all – so He simplified the Guidebook for us. Let me show you how.

New Testament Scriptures:
1. Read Matthew 22:37-40.   Please write it word-for-word in the space below.

2. Who is speaking in this passage?

3. <u>What are the two commandments He gives?</u>

<u>According to verse 40, upon what is all the rest of the Word based?</u>

See how simple! As my friend reminds me it's not always easy, but it is simple. As you read the Bible, you are guided through each command, each instruction, exhortation, or warning to love God and/or love others with His love. It's that simple. Let's try it.

Old Testament Scriptures:

5. <u>Read Exodus 20:1-17, the Ten Commandments. Chart them by listing them in their proper category below.</u>

Verses	LOVE GOD		Verses	LOVE OTHERS

See, every command falls under one of these two commandments.
(God is always right!)

Let's try a story in the New Testament.

New Testament Scriptures:

6. Read Luke 7:36-38, 44-48. What basic truths about loving God did you discover? What truths about loving others did you see?

7. Read Romans 12. (It's a bit long so don't linger, just read it through.) How is the instruction in verses 1 and 2 a fulfillment of the first commandment to love God?

How are verses 3-21 the guide to keeping the second commandment to love others?

8. <u>Read Romans 5:5</u>.   <u>Because we've received Christ by faith, what marvelous thing has He done according to verse 5?</u>

9. <u>Please read 1 Corinthians 13:4-8</u>. <u>List how God's love, given through the Holy Spirit to you, is defined.</u>

<u>What does this mean to you personally as far as being able to fulfill the great commandments of God to love?</u>

<u>Today how can you show love to particular people in your life –especially the one who is hard to love?</u>

 ## Walking with Others

See how simple this Guidebook is to follow! In every passage, ask: what is this telling me to think, to say, or to do so I am loving God and loving others.   All the other commandments are simply showing us how to love. It's not always easy, because we still love ourselves and there is still a devil who seeks our harm (don't worry, he's defeated, just be aware), but it is simple.

Not only that, but the good Word tells us God has given us His love with which to love Him and others, His Holy Spirit indwelling to empower us to obey His two commandments to love. What an awesome God of love!! He has given us His very own supernatural love, so we can love Him and love others – just like Jesus. I just love Him so much, don't you?

~~~~~~

ALABASTER HEART

Nothing to Thee can I bring,
Holding to Thy hand I cling.
No alabaster box have I
To break open and anoint Thee by.
I have only the heart Thou gave to me
To live, to love, to honor Thee.
Take it, my Lord, it is Thine own;
Humbly I lay it before Thy Throne.

Conni Hudson
a bondservant of Christ

Journeying With Jesus Through the Basics   Week Four Day Four
                                              The Simplicity of the Word

 Walking in Prayer

Isn't your heart filled to overflowing with love and gratitude to your great God of love? Spend some time on your knees praising and thanking Him for His simple, awesome plan of love.

Walking in the Psalms

Read and meditate on stanzas 13-17 of Psalm 119 (verses 97-136). How does the psalmist express his love of God through his love of God's Word? You cannot love God if you don't love His Word for He has "magnified His Word according to all His name." (Psalm 138:2).

Stanza 13 (verses 97-104)	Stanza 15 (verses 113-120)	Stanza 17 (verses 129-136)

Stanza 14 (verses 105-112)	Stanza 16 (verses 121-128)	

Walking in Wonder

What questions do you have concerning today's study?

My fellow journeyers, I commend you for all your hard study!!
You are storing up His word in your heart and it's a great thing
I am so happy for you! Keep up the good work.

Walking Through Today: Journaling the Journey

_____

_____

_____

_____

_____

_____

_____

_____

_____

_____

_____

_____

_____

_____

_____

_____

_____

_____

_____

_____

_____

Walking Through Today: Journaling the Journey   Date:_____

Our Response to the Word

*For the word of the cross is foolishness to those who are perishing,
but to us who are being saved it is the power of God.*
I Corinthians 1:18

 Walking with Him through the Word

Basic facts about the Bible:

> It is one book, comprised of 66 books
>   39 Old Testament and 27 New Testament
> (easy trick to help you remember: 3x9 (O.T. number) = 27 (N.T. number)
> Subject of Bible: God (We can know Him through His Word)
> Inspired by God, it was written by 40 men over a period of 1,500 years. Some men were fishermen, farmers, slaves, and some were kings. They could not have known one another, but their words never contradicted. Instead, they made up the complete, revealed Word of God.
> The Old Testament was written originally in Hebrew and a bit of Aramaic.
> The New Testament was written originally in Koine Greek.
> The Old Testament was written by prophets inspired by God.
> The New Testament was written by the apostles and New Testament prophets, those with apostolic authority. It was also inspired by God.

There is much to learn about the Bible, how it was written, handed down, and preserved intact for us. Many people gave their lives so we can hold this book in our hands. Many evil men have tried to destroy it from the face of the earth, but it cannot be done. Their work was in vain. It is the Word of God! He protects it. *"The grass withers and the flowers fade but the Word of God endures forever"* (Isaiah 40:8). We are called and privileged to be faithful to it.

1. <u>What are we to do with this marvelous Guidebook? What is to be our response to this provision? Read the following Scriptures and see what responses you can discover.</u>

(I know there are a lot of verses to look up. You might want to divide your study time into segments: a few verses in the morning, a few in the afternoon, and a few in the evening. You just don't want to miss any – His Word is so good!)

Old Testament Scriptures:

Psalm 1:2

Psalm 17:4

Psalm 40:8

Psalm 111:2

Psalm 119:11

Isaiah 34:16

Jeremiah 15:16

New Testament Scriptures:

Matthew 4:4

Matthew 7:24

John 14:15

Acts 17:11

Romans 15:4

I Peter 2:2

II Peter 1:4

I John 5:13

Jude 1:3

Revelation 1:3

How is the Word magnified to you today as you have studied these passages?

Do you have a Bible reading plan? What reading plan can you put in place so you are in the Word every day?

Walking with Others

Wow! The Word plays a vital role in the believer's life, doesn't it? We come to faith in God by hearing and believing it. We, then, are called to listen, read, search, study, meditate, memorize, defend, obey – in other words, live by it. It is our Guidebook, graciously provided by our Father. The promises of the abundant life of joy and peace are ours to enjoy now as we respond to His Word. His comfort and security is ours as He guides us in and through the trials and struggles of our journey. His Word is proof of His love for us and our response to His Word is proof of our love of Him. *Journeying with Jesus* is walking in and with Him according to His good Word.

~~~~~~

READ YOUR BIBLE

➤ Slowly, with mind alert.
➤ Carefully and with prayer.
➤ Expectantly and with anticipation.
➤ In a spirit of enjoyment.
➤ Eager to respond inwardly.
➤ Seeking a personal message.
➤ Repeating aloud verses which strike fire.
➤ Keeping a definite time each day for reading.
➤ Copying out a key verse to carry with you for re-reading through the day.

Selected [10]

Walking in Prayer

As you've looked at the importance of God's Word to your journey, what is your response? Spend some time in prayer, thanking God for His Word. You might want to ask Him to open the eyes of your understanding, increase your desire and love for His Word and help you obey it.   The Lord delights to answer the prayers of His beloved children, so pray. Write it out here or on your journal pages, if you'd like.

Walking in the Psalms

Finish reading Psalm 119. Notice what it tells you about responding to the Word. How did the psalmist respond to God's Word? (You might want to go through the entire psalm someday and list his different responses.)

Stanza 18 (verses 137-144)	Stanza 20 (verses 153-160)	Stanza 22 (verses 169-176)

Stanza 19 (verses 145-152)	Stanza 21 (verses 161-168)	

Walking in Wonder

I wonder…

Walking Through Today: Journaling the Journey

_____

_____

_____

_____

_____

_____

_____

_____

_____

_____

_____

_____

_____

_____

_____

_____

_____

_____

_____

Walking Through Today: Journaling the Journey   Date:_____

Week Five

Prayer

Day One   The Privilege and Purpose of Prayer

Day Two   The Person of Prayer

Day Three   The Pattern of Prayer

Day Four   The Principles of Prayer

Day Five   The Promise of Prayer

The Privilege and Purpose of Prayer

If you abide in Me, and My words abide in you,
ask whatever you wish, and it will be done for you.
John 15:7

 ## Walking with Him through the Word

Remember your child's first words? Remember your loved ones last words? Remember the first time someone you loved said, "I love you?" Remember the joy of simple conversation with your best friend? Communication is vital to our lives, isn't it? Communication with our Lord, even more so. He speaks with us through His Word and has given us the way of response – prayer. What a pleasure this provision is as we are *journeying with Jesus.* To know, as we journey, we are never alone and never out of His earshot means... well... everything. Let's discover the basics about this great privilege of prayer.

New Testament Scripture:

1. Please read 1 John 5:13-15. According to verse 13, how did we receive the great privilege of the provision of prayer?

Once we put our hand in His, the doors of communication were opened.

What is our confidence as stated in verses 14 and 15?

2. <u>Read John 14:13</u>. <u>Jesus is speaking</u>. <u>He is encouraging the disciples</u>. <u>What promise does He give?</u>

<u>What is the purpose of praying in the Son's name?</u>

<u>How do you suppose prayer in the Son's name would glorify the Father?</u>

3. <u>According to the above verse (John 14:13), John 14:14, and John 16:23, in whose name do we pray?</u>

<u>According to John 16:23, to Whom do we pray?</u>

4. <u>How do you see this provision of God in your own life?</u>

 ## Walking with Others

The awesome provision of prayer is a privilege given to the believer in Christ, to those who are *journeying with Jesus* hand-in-Hand. God promises to hear and respond to the prayers of His children. When His children pray in the name of Christ, they are praying according to His character. We know from His Word He is good and He always does good. He is faithful to keep His Word. He is trustworthy to care perfectly for His own. Knowing who He is – His character – causes us to want only His will, for it will be all that is good and right. So when we pray in His name, we are asking for His will to be done over and above all we ask for in prayer. In fact, we want to line up our prayers with His will. We aren't asking God to be a magic genie giving us our wishes. Instead we are praying in His name for His will to be revealed and done in every situation.

What a privilege it is to be allowed, through prayer, to be part of God's great will in life. If you prayed for someone's salvation, for instance, and they gave their life to God, you didn't save him, but you had the joy and privilege of being part of God's good will. If you prayed for a child as he struggled through rebellion, you had the privilege of being part of God's plan and work in that person's life as God wooed him to Himself. If a church body was floundering and you prayed, you became part of the work as He accomplished His will for that church.

The work and results are always God's. He will always do what is right and best according to His character and for His good purpose. You merely have the privilege of being part of what He is doing through your prayers.

What happens when your prayers are answered? God is glorified. He is put on display. His love, power, honor, comfort, holiness, goodness, mercy, and justice are shining forth for all the world to see. That is the purpose of prayer. How glorious – what a privilege is the provision of prayer.

Walking in Prayer

Knowing the awesome privilege and purpose of prayer, won't you pray? Spend some time meditating on the character qualities of the Lord listed below. Learning of God's character will help you praise Him for who He is, instill thankfulness in your heart, and deepen your knowledge of Him. As you know Him better, you will better know how to pray.

~~~~~~

Character Qualities of God

God Is:	Old Testament Passage	New Testament Passage
Eternal	Deuteronomy 32:40	Romans 1:20
Good	Psalm 33:5	Matthew 7:11
Gracious	Psalm 84:11	Ephesians 1:6
Immutable	Ecclesiastes 3:14	Romans 11:29
Love	Psalm 42:8	I John 4:8
Merciful	Psalm 57:10	II Corinthians 1:3
Sovereign	Exodus 15:18	Ephesains 4:6
Truthful	Psalm 33:4	I Corinthians 1:9
Wise	Job 9:4	I Timothy 1:17

These are just a few of God's attributes. As you study His Word and come across more, make your own list to refer to as you pray and worship Him.

(You may continue your prayer here.)

Walking through the Psalms

Read the prayer of Psalm 61. What does the Psalmist know about his God that causes him to use the provision of prayer? How do you see his understanding of this high privilege of prayer?

Walking in Wonder

Please note any questions you might have as a result of your study today.

Walking Through Today: Journaling the Journey

_____

_____

_____

_____

_____

_____

_____

_____

_____

_____

_____

_____

_____

_____

_____

_____

_____

_____

_____

_____

Walking Through Today: Journaling the Journey   Date:_____

 Walking Through Today: Journaling the Journey

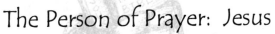

The Person of Prayer: Jesus
The next morning Jesus awoke long before daybreak
and went out alone into the wilderness to pray.
Mark 1:35

Walking with Him through the Word

Many of you had the privilege of growing up in a home where the provision of prayer was demonstrated before you. But, as wonderful as that is, we have a better, more perfect example, in our Lord Jesus Christ. He was a person of prayer. The gospels are a testimony to His lifestyle of prayer. He enjoyed the incredible provision and we can follow in His steps.

New Testament Scripture:

1. <u>From the following verses, what can you learn from Jesus' lifestyle of prayer?</u>

<u>Matthew 14:23</u>

<u>Mark 1:35</u>

<u>Luke 5:16</u>

<u>Luke 6:12</u>

<u>Luke 23:46</u>

<u>How is Jesus' example in the above passages an encouragement to you?</u>

<u>What can you do to make prayer a priority?</u>

2. Please read John 11:41-42. What did Jesus know?

If you are in Christ, then what can you know?

3. Please read through Hebrews 4:16. Through our relationship with the Person of prayer, what are we given provision to do?

How does knowing you can come boldly before the throne of your Father God encourage you to pray?

4. To see one more exciting truth, please turn to Hebrews 7:24, 25. What is Jesus always doing for us?

What is your heart response to knowing that the Lord Jesus Christ is ever-interceding for you?

 ## Walking with Others

Reading through the gospels, you become a witness to the Lord Jesus' life of prayer. He depended on this provision as He journeyed with the Father while here on earth. What an example for us. He made prayer His priority. In full submission to His Father, He sought communion with Him always. Knowing He had open, constant access to His Father, Jesus nevertheless relished and sought out "alone times of intimacy" with Him.

We see Jesus pray at His baptism (which began His public ministry), throughout His ministry, and at the end of His public ministry (when He prayed and gave up His spirit on the cross). He understood and sought to show, by His example, the privilege and priority of prayer. Doesn't He make you excited about prayer and hungry to have a lifestyle of communion with your heavenly Father? Let us follow His example.

~~~~~~

> If Jesus, the strong Son of God, felt it necessary to rise before the breaking of the day to pour out His heart to God in prayer, how much more ought you to pray unto Him who is the Giver of every good and perfect gift, and who has promised all things necessary for our good. What Jesus gathered into His life from His prayers we can never know, but this we do know, that the prayerless life is a powerless life. A prayerless life may be a noisy life, and fuss around a great deal; but such a life is far removed from him who, by day and night, prayed to God.

Mrs. Charles Cowman in *Streams in the Desert* [11]

Walking in Prayer

Like the Person of Prayer, the Lord Jesus Christ, your Lord and Savior, won't you make prayer a priority? Won't you come alone now to be with your Father? Pour out your heart to Him either in the space below or on your journal page.

Walking in the Psalms

Take time to read and ponder Psalm 121 please. What did the psalmist know about the Person of Prayer?

 ## Walking in Wonder

Any questions?

👣 Walking Through Today: Journaling the Journey

_____

_____

_____

_____

_____

_____

_____

_____

_____

_____

_____

_____

_____

_____

_____

_____

_____

_____

_____

_____

_____

Walking Through Today: Journaling the Journey   Date:_____

The Pattern of Prayer
"Pray like this: . . ."
Luke 11:2

 ## Walking with Him through the Word

In Luke 11 the Bible gives an account of Jesus praying. As He was praying, the disciples, having witnessed Jesus' lifestyle of prayer, asked Him to teach them to pray. And, Jesus gave them a pattern to follow. Matthew also records this pattern in his Gospel. Today, let's look at this pattern.

New Testament Scripture:

1. Please read Matthew 6:5-7. What three-word phrase is repeated?

Praying is assumed, it is an act of obedience. It is a supernatural response to our restored relationship with God.

Now read Matthew 6:7 again. Consider that this was the first time Jesus gave His disciples the "pattern of prayer." What strong exhortation did Jesus give along with the "pattern?"

From this verse we know this prayer isn't a formula or a mantra, but simply a pattern, an example of principle aspects of prayer.

2. <u>Read through both the Matthew 6:9-13 and Luke 11:2-4 "pattern of prayer." The NASB, KJV, and other original manuscripts add to the Matthew passage, "For Thine is the kingdom and the power and the glory forever. Amen." From these passages, please answer the following questions.</u>

<u>To whom is the prayer addressed in both passages?</u>

<u>Who would "our" include?</u>

<u>Where is He?</u>

<u>As this prayer begins, how is He honored?</u>

This is a picture of praise. Praise is a key aspect of prayer – knowing, recognizing, and honoring Him – as God Almighty. It is vital we understand and have Him in His rightful place, as Lord, both in our hearts and in our prayers.

<u>Having the Father in His rightful place as Lord, leads to the next pattern piece. What is it?</u>

God is in His rightful place when we humble ourselves in submission to Him. His children recognize His perfection and seek only to line up with His will. In heaven, where there is no sin, His will is done perfectly, and that should be the desire of all His children while here on earth.

<u>What is the next piece of the pattern which speaks to His daily provision?</u>

<u>What might "daily bread" include?</u>

<u>What is the next pattern piece?</u>

<u>Did you notice it is conditional?</u>

Recognizing who our heavenly Father is, the privilege it is to be His, causes us to desire only His will. We realize all our needs are met in Him, so we seek Him for them. All of this causes us to realize how far short we fall from His glory as we seek our own way. This calls for a petition of forgiveness. Within this understanding of just how much we are forgiven, there should then be an instant realization, an awareness, of the need to forgive others. If there is not, that would be a clear indication of a problem within the petitioner's own heart.

<u>And what is the final pattern piece?</u>

God never tempts us to sin. He empowers us not to sin and enables us to see temptation for what it is and run to Him for rescue.

The added phrase in the NASB gives the reason for all the pieces of the pattern. What is it?

He is God! He has the power to answer these prayer petitions and through His answers, He is glorified. Amen (so be it).

Now, list the pattern pieces below in order to see the complete picture. Match the pattern pieces to the categories into which they fall.

Category	Pattern Piece
Praise	
Allegiance & Submission	
Petition & Intercession	
Confession & Forgiveness	
Deliverance & Protection	
Worship	

3. <u>How does Jesus giving you a pattern for prayer show His love for you?</u>

 ## Walking with Others

What a complete pattern the Lord Jesus Christ has given His disciples (followers) both in word and by His lifestyle. Within His pattern He shows us the succinct elements in prayer.

As you read through the New Testament and see the prayers of the apostles recorded there, you will notice two things:

a. There is never a rote repetition of this "pattern of prayer." It is not used as a mantra or formula.

b. Every prayer does not necessarily include each and every pattern piece, but we see through the lifestyle of the petitioner, all the pieces are understood and implied.

The great exhortation is to:

-Pray, realizing how important it is in your relationship with God in bringing Him glory through your life.
-Pray, purposely using His pattern as your guide.
-Pray, above all, for God's will to be done on earth as it is in heaven.

Walking in Prayer

Please read Daniel's prayer in the Old Testament: Daniel 9:4-19. Note below the pieces of the pattern you see in this Old Testament saint's prayer. The pattern has always been there. It was just articulated by Christ. Using the pieces of the pattern, pray to your glorious Father all that is on your heart today – He is listening.

Walking in the Psalms

As you consider the ultimate result of the "pattern of prayer," – God's will to be done on earth, thus bringing Him glory – meditate on Psalm 8.

How is His glory described? How is His glory revealed on earth? How can you show forth His glory today?

God's Glory		
How Described	How Revealed	How to Show Today

Walking in Wonder

????

I applaud you, journeyers, for your diligence in study.
I know these lessons are long. Praise God for your faithfulness to persevere.
What a blessing His Word will be as you hide it in your heart.

Walking Through Today: Journaling the Journey

_____

_____

_____

_____

_____

_____

_____

_____

_____

_____

_____

_____

_____

_____

_____

_____

_____

_____

_____

_____

_____

_____

Walking Through Today: Journaling the Journey

Date:_____

The Principles of Prayer

And so I tell you, keep on asking, and you will be given what you ask for.
Keep on looking, and you will find. Keep on knocking, and the door will be opened.
Luke 11:9

 ## Walking with Him through the Word

Surrounded by the "pattern of prayer" in Matthew and Luke are two basic principles of prayer: privacy and persistency (love all the "P" words?). The examples of both of these principles are seen in Christ's life. He spent much time alone in prayer and, in Gethsemane, He persisted until convinced of His Father's will. Today let's examine these two principles.

New Testament Scripture:

1. Read Matthew 6:5-7. What is a hypocrite? And how is hypocrisy described here?

In verse 6 what does Jesus exhort the true believer to do? What is the result?

Jesus often prayed publicly, as did the saints of the Old and New Testament. What then is the principle? While public, corporate prayer has a place and purpose, it is to come from a sincere heart for a specific purpose and is always to glorify God, not self. Most prayer is to be private and personal, with the reward being His answer which glorifies Him on earth as His will is done.

<u>According to verse 7, what is another thing people of other religions do (these people would be non-believers, the hypocrites who worship for the glory of self and not for God's glory)?</u>

This forbids the idea of using a mantra to "center" a person to hear God's voice. This also forbids the idea of merely repeating prayer or praises with no thought put into what is being prayed. (Note: there is a place for repetition of a prayer when one is thoughtfully, sincerely, praying these words from the heart and not just repeating the prayer for repetition's sake.)

2. <u>Please read the story and application Jesus told after He gave the pattern of prayer in Luke 11:5-10. According to verse 9 what basic principle is Jesus teaching?</u>

Jesus contrasts the sinful neighbor who only responds begrudgingly to persistence with the heavenly Father, who loves to give good gifts, through the Spirit, to His children in answer to their prayer.

<u>Why, then, do you suppose He calls for persistence instead of just giving you what you ask the moment you ask?</u>

Have you ever persisted in prayer only to have God change your prayer? He is taking you on a journey of faith so you will learn to trust Him, to wait on His will, and to glorify Him.

3. <u>What does Romans 8:26-27 tell you about yourself concerning prayer?</u>

<u>So who prays for you and why?</u>

4. <u>According to Romans 8:28-29 what is God's will?</u>

<u>What is the purpose of His will</u>

 Walking with Others

What an awesome God. How unsearchable are His ways! He calls us to pray, to persist in our prayers. As we pray the generalities, the Holy Spirit prays the particulars, in complete harmony with the will of God. Of course God will answer and do what is right and best in every situation for the purpose of spiritually growing us to be Christlike. He is restoring us to the person He created us to be without sin's stain, restoring our wonderful relationship with Himself. Wow!

Walking in Prayer

Spend some time alone with your Father responding to what you have just learned. This is the Word of God. These are the basic principles of His provision. Will you line up your life with His truth? Pray now for the faith to persist in belief and trust. Pour out your heart to your Lord.

Walking in the Psalms

Please read and meditate on Psalm 16 today. How do you see the principle of persistence in the psalmist prayer?

 ## Walking in Wonder

I wonder. . . .

Walking Through Today: Journaling the Journey

_____

_____

_____

_____

_____

_____

_____

_____

_____

_____

_____

_____

_____

_____

_____

_____

_____

_____

_____

_____

_____

Walking Through Today: Journaling the Journey   Date:_____

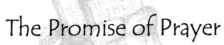

The Promise of Prayer

*"Yes,. Ask Me for anything in My name
and I will do it."*
John 14:14

Walking with Him through the Word

When someone promises you something, for the most part, you can count on it. When God promises you something, you can ALWAYS count on it. And God has promised His children something concerning prayer. Let's see what He's promised.

New Testament Scripture:

1. <u>Please read the promise to believers in 1 John 5:13-15</u>. <u>What is His promise concerning prayer in verse 15?</u>

<u>The promise is conditioned on what in verse 14?</u>

His will (i.e. what pleases Him) brings Him glory, and we know it is always what is good and best for us. Once again, this is the simple truth. But what if our prayer is 'in His will' (i.e. we know it is from His Word), but it isn't answered? What could be the reason?

Old Testament Scripture:

2. <u>Please read Daniel 10:1-14 please</u>. <u>What was the problem in verses 12 and 13 concerning Daniel's prayer being answered?</u>

Spiritual warfare delays answers. But they, the answers, are assured if the prayers are in the will of God as stated in His Word. All we are called to do is stand firm in our faith, persist in prayer, and wait.

267

New Testament Scripture:

3. <u>Is God's answer ever "no?"</u> <u>What do you see in the following verses?</u>

<u>Matthew 26:39</u>

<u>2 Corinthians 12:7-9</u>

<u>James 1:6, 7</u>

4. <u>There can be some hindrances to prayers being answered</u>. <u>According to the following verses what could these hindrances be</u>?

<u>Matthew 6:7</u>

<u>Matthew 6:14-15</u>

John 15:7

James 4:2b-3

1 Peter 3:7

1 Peter 3:12

5. If all is well – all hindrances are dealt with through repentance and obedience – what promises will be realized if you pray, according to the following verses?

John 14:14

<u>Romans 8:28-29</u>

<u>Philippians 4:6, 7</u>

 ## Walking with Others

Rest in the promises of God. He has promised to hear and answer your prayers. Jesus Christ died to secure your adoption and sits at the right-hand of God ever-interceding for you. He has given you the Holy Spirit to intercede for you causing your prayers to be in harmony with His will. As you persist in prayer, if need be, your Father will change your prayers to line up with His will, causing you to realize "His grace is sufficient." Knowing God will take care of all spiritual opposition, and as you remove all hindrances, you can rest assured in His perfect time the answer will be realized. Aren't you thrilled to know you ever have His ear? Aren't you excited to, like Christ, live a lifestyle of prayer? 1 Thessalonians 5:17 tells you to "pray without ceasing." Colossians 3:2 says "set your mind on things above." This, is the heart attitude of a person of prayer and is seen in the example of your Lord Jesus Christ. So let's pray!

~~~~~~

> Delays are not refusals; many a prayer is registered, and underneath it the words: *My time is not yet come.* God has a set time as well as a set purpose, and He who orders the bounds of our habitation orders also the time of our deliverance.
>
> Mrs. Charles Cowman in *Streams in the Desert*[12]

Walking in Prayer

Read and meditate on Paul's prayer in Ephesians 3:14-20. Use this prayer as a springboard for your own.

Walking in Prayer

Walking in the Psalms

Please read and meditate on Psalm 116 today. How do you see the psalmist trust in the promises of God to hear his prayer?

 ## Walking in Wonder

Please note any questions you might have. We want to help you find the answers.

Walking Through Today: Journaling the Journey

Walking Through Today: Journaling the Journey   Date:_____

Week Six

The Body of Christ

How Firm a Foundation

*For no man can lay a foundation
other than the one which is laid,
which is Jesus Christ.*
1 Corinthians 3:11

 ## Walking with Him through the Word

We have a backpack of provisions given us by God for *journeying with Jesus* until we get to our eternal home: the Word, prayer, the indwelling Spirit, and friends to walk beside us on the *journey*. In Scripture these friends are called the church. The Church is not a physical building where we go to worship. The Church is the people of God who, together, make a spiritual building. Today let us examine some of the facts of this precious provision.

New Testament Scripture:

1. Please read Matthew 7:24-27 as Jesus tells a story. According to these verses, on what are you to build a house to insure its safety?

2. Read Matthew 16:15-18. When Jesus asked Peter whom he believed Jesus to be, what was his reply?

According to verse 18, Jesus declared that upon this truth He would build what?

3. Read 1 Corinthians 3:11. Who is the foundation of the church?

4. Please read Ephesians 2:20-22. How is Jesus described?

Who makes up the rest of the foundation?

Who is the house of God?

In verse 21 how are we described?

5. Please read Romans 1:7, Ephesians 1:1, Philippians 1:1, and Colossians 1:1. To whom are these letters addressed?

Saints, holy people, are synonyms for believers – those who have put their faith in Christ. **Holy** is the Greek word, *Hagios,* and means 'set-apart for God's use.' Each person who receives Christ as Lord and Savior is set-apart by God, from the world to Himself, so becoming holy – a saint.

6. How does 1 Peter 2:4-6 confirm the truths you have just studied?

7. Are you a living stone in God's house? How do you know?

8. What does it mean to you to be called holy, to be a living stone in the house of God?

 Walking with Others

Our good and gracious God has given us friends for the journey, our fellow believers who make up the church. Using a word picture in Matthew 7, Jesus explained a building is only as secure as its foundation. Later, in Matthew 16, when Peter declared Jesus to be the Christ, Jesus declared Himself to be the Rock upon which He would build His church. In both Ephesians and 1 Peter, Jesus is described as the Rock, the Cornerstone of the foundation of the church. The apostles and the prophets, aligned with Christ, first took the gospel message to others. So they helped make up the foundation of the church.

As people hear and put their faith in Christ they become living stones in the building of God – the temple where His presence, His Holy Spirit, dwells. Together as a church we worship Him, proclaim Him, love Him, and house Him in our hearts.

Walking in Prayer

As you spend time in prayer today, take time to respond to the gift of this provision –
the gift of being a living stone in the spiritual building of God.

Walking through the Psalms

Read and meditate on the joyful praise of Psalm 98. Use this as a springboard for your own time of praise. As the psalmist did, won't you make a list of your praises? I am sure today, at the top of your list, will be that you have been privileged to be a living stone in the spiritual house of God.

Walking in Wonder

?.

?

?

Walking Through Today: Journaling the Journey

_____

_____

_____

_____

_____

_____

_____

_____

_____

_____

_____

_____

_____

_____

_____

_____

_____

_____

_____

_____

Walking Through Today: Journaling the Journey   Date:_____

Walking Through Today: Journaling the Journey

The Body of Christ

*Now you are Christ's body,
and individually members of it.*
1 Corinthians 12:27

 ## Walking with Him through the Word

Aren't word pictures helpful? The imagery provides us with a concrete way to grasp a concept or truth. In addition to the word picture of the church being a building, there is another word picture or analogy given to help us understand the church and how we are to function together. To view this word picture let's hike a trail together through the book of Ephesians.

New Testament Scripture:

1. According to Ephesians 1:22-23, how is Christ and the church pictured?

2. Please read Ephesians 2:7-9. How do we become united with Christ, a part of His body?

3. According to Ephesians 2:14-17, what 2 groups make up the body of Christ?

4. According to Ephesians 3:6, how is God's plan summarized?

5. <u>Please read Ephesians 4:1-6</u>. <u>Because we are the body of Christ, what are we to do and why according to these verses?</u>

As the Body	
We are to do:	Because:

As you look at the "to do" list, please be reminded from the "because" list that as the body you are indwelt by the Holy Spirit of God who has given you the love of God and the power of God to do and be all God calls you to do and to be.

Walking with Others

This word picture makes it easy to understand God's intent for the church. In eternity past God the Father, Son, and Holy Spirit planned for us. Through Christ's death, burial, and resurrection, He provided the way of salvation, forgiveness, and adoption into God's family. Before God implemented His plan to unite us into one body through the cross, He, in His wisdom, orchestrated His plan step-by-step.

First, God promised to send a Redeemer to save us from our sinful state and bring us into the family of God. Everyone who believed and put their trust in this promise of a Redeemer was saved – looking forward to that promise being fulfilled. Then, God raised up the nation of Israel though Abraham, Isaac, and Jacob, declaring them to be His chosen people through whom would come the promised Messiah (Christ). He then gave the Israelites rules of law and worship (called the Old Covenant or the Law) to keep them separated (set apart) as His own people until the promise would be fulfilled by sending Christ Jesus to die on the cross for our sins (establishing the New Covenant). When Christ was raised from the dead this proved His diety and the fulfillment of the promise. God had accomplished our salvation.

Jesus Christ, as our Savior, is also our Head (as we saw in Ephesians 1:22 above). We, as believers, are His body. This plan was and is for everyone who believes – Jew or Gentile. No more is there a dividing wall (Old Covenant of Law – refer to Ephesians 2:14) needed to separate. Jesus Christ united us together as one body under His Headship, sending His Holy Spirit to indwell us and to seal us, thus guaranteeing our unity now and for all eternity (New Covenant of Grace).

Our response, as His body, is to preserve this unity. As we lead a life worthy of our calling as His body, united in peace, He is glorified as Almighty God and others will be drawn to Him as Lord and Savior by our love and treatment of one another (John 13:35). What is one thing all men want? Peace of heart. Where is it found? In Christ. How is it revealed? Through His body living in harmony and loving one another, and through sharing the good news of the perfect plan of God with those who don't know Him.

Walking in Prayer

Ephesians 1:15-23 is Paul's prayer for the church. That includes you. Meditate on this prayer. Consider what he is saying, using it as a springboard for your own prayer today. Use the space below or your journal to articulate your thoughts.

Walking through the Psalms

Please read and meditate on Psalm 133 today. List the results of living in unity (harmony) with one another. Consider how you can promote unity in the body today, remembering its results.

 Walking in Wonder

Any questions today?

Walking Through Today: Journaling the Journey

Walking Through Today: Journaling the Journey   Date:_____

The Equipping of the Body

*And He gave some as apostles, and some as prophets,
and some as evangelists, and some as pastors and teachers,
for the equipping of the saints for the work of service,
to the building up of the body of Christ*
Ephesians 4:11-12

(Precious friend, this day's lesson reinforces part of what you learned in Week 3. Remember, review is good! It helps cement truth. Plus it helps us see the Bible as a whole. So, review with rejoicing and let the Lord add to your library of knowledge and understanding.)

Walking with Him through the Word

I come from a family of five – my daddy, mama, sister, brother, and myself. We each had certain talents and gifts, and together we made one family. My daddy had the gift of wisdom. Mama: the gift of practicality. My sister: the gift of responsibility. My brother had the gift of laughter and joy. And I, the baby, had the gift of well – being the baby. I am so thankful for gifted parents who used their gifts and taught us to use ours to preserve the unity of the body of our family.

In the body of Christ, the church, God has spiritually gifted each of us. As we live together, work together, using our giftedness, the unity of the body is maintained. Continuing on the trail of Ephesians, let's examine some of the basics of our giftedness.

New Testament Scripture:

1. <u>Please read Ephesians 4:1-6 (you read it yesterday and it's a good place to "pick up the trail"). According to verse 1, as we are *journeying with Jesus*, how are we to walk?</u>

<u>According to verse 3 what are we to make every effort to do?</u>

What do verses 4-6 say about how are we united?

2. Now please read Ephesians 4 verses 7-12. Though we are united, we are uniquely gifted. From verse 7 and 8, who gifted us?

And according to verses 7 and 8, who did He gift?

From verse 11, list the gifted men God gave to the church (these are saints who are given gifts by the Holy Spirit).

And what is their responsibility according to verse 12?

How would they equip the body of Christ? What do they have in common?

3. Now please read Ephesians 4:13-16? As this equipping and working continues, what will be the result according to verse 13?

As we are taught the Word, taught to know and love Christ, we will become spiritually mature – Christlike in character – loving Him and one another. What a great result.

This spiritual maturity will keep us from what according to verse 14?

Instead, what will happen, what will be our experience according to verse 15?

How is the work of giftedness summarized in verse 16?

4. How are you promoting unity in the body of Christ?

5. <u>What does knowing you are gifted by God to serve in the body mean to you?</u>

6. <u>Will you seek to serve?</u>

Walking with Others

In the Old Testament, beginning in Genesis 12, we read of God raising up a nation, Israel, to be His chosen people, through whom would come the Redeemer, Jesus Christ (the Messiah). The Old Covenant of Law was given to Israel through Moses (see Exodus through Deuteronomy). This group of social, ceremonial, and dietary laws were used by God to protect Israel from the influences of the sinful world system until Messiah would come.

And come He did! Christ's birth, death, burial, and resurrection ushered in the New Covenant of Grace. No longer was the Old Covenant of Law needed (Hebrews 8-10). Under the New Covenant of Grace, Jew and Gentile, by His grace, through faith, enter into God's family, into the body of Christ. God's love, through the indwelling Holy Spirit, fills the hearts of those who receive Him by faith, and as His body, they are united under His headship and gifted to serve one another in love.

As they serve in unity, the whole body grows spiritually in their understanding of the Word and in their personal relationship with the Lord, and through this unity of the body Christ Jesus is glorified and draws others to Himself. Isn't it wonderful to know as you are *journeying with Jesus* your unity reveals and glorifies your Lord?! You are part of the eternal plan and purpose of God! This is why it is key to "preserve the unity of faith in the bond of peace" (Ephesians 4:3).

Walking in Prayer

In Ephesians 3:14-20 Paul prayed for the body. For what did he pray and how can you make this your prayer today?

Walking through the Psalms

Please meditate on Psalm 134 today. Spend time praising God for the privilege of being united with Christ and one another. Praise Him for His gifts and the privilege of using those gifts to serve one another in the body.

 Walking in Wonder

I wonder...

Walking Through Today: Journaling the Journey

_____

_____

_____

_____

_____

_____

_____

_____

_____

_____

_____

_____

_____

_____

_____

_____

_____

_____

_____

Walking Through Today: Journaling the Journey   Date:_____

Live Worthy of the Calling

...walk in a manner worthy of the calling
with which you have been called
.Ephesians 4:1

 ## Walking with Him through the Word

Journeying with Jesus as a living stone, as a part of the body of Christ is privilege beyond compare. It is also a whole new way of living – totally opposite from the world's way. And we need one another to help us as we walk, so together we glorify God.

The Bible is filled with "one anothers" to show us how to walk or, as Ephesians 4:1 puts it, "to lead a life worthy of our calling." Let's look at some of those 'one anothers.' (We'll hike the "one another" trail today.)

New Testament Scripture:

1. <u>Please read the following verses and note the "one anothers" you see.</u>

<u>John 13:4, 12-15</u>

<u>John 13:34-35</u>

<u>Romans 12:10</u>

<u>Romans 12:16</u>

<u>Galatians 5:26</u>

<u>Galatians 6:2-3</u>

<u>Ephesians 4:32</u>

2. <u>What practical steps can you take to do these things today?</u>

3. Is there anything in your life you need to change - someone to forgive, encourage, serve, honor, make peace with – so you are a "one another" person of obedience? Write it down, so you will remember to act upon it.

4. How does the indwelling Holy Spirit work in your life to make you a "one another" person?

 ## Walking with Others

These are only a few of the "one anothers" found in the Word. The Lord, our Head, desires for us to preserve the unity of the body by loving, serving, and forgiving just as He has loved, served, and forgiven us. By doing this, the world will see the great difference Christ makes in our lives. They will then, be drawn to the One Who can promote such unity.

Now, here is the incredible part! It is impossible for us to do this on our own, isn't it? That is why God gave us the provision of His indwelling Spirit, to empower us to "walk in the Spirit" (yield to His good Word in obedience) (Galatians 5:16 and Ephesians 5:18), and as we do, we will be able – abundantly graced - to obey all the "one anothers!" To God be the glory – great things He has done!

~~~~~~

Now may the God who gives perseverance and encouragement grant you to be of the same mind with one another according to Christ Jesus, so that with one accord you may with one voice glorify the God and Father of our Lord Jesus Christ. Therefore, accept one another, just as Christ also accepted us to the glory of God.

God, through Paul in Romans 15:5-7

Walking in Prayer

Romans 15:13 is my prayer for you and can be yours for one another in the body. Please meditate on this prayer and if led, use it as a springboard for your own prayer.

> *Now may the God of hope fill you with all joy and peace in believing,*
> *so that you will abound in hope by the power of the Holy Spirit.*

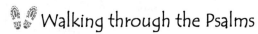 Walking through the Psalms

Please read Psalm 121. How can you use this Psalm to pray for one another? Won't you do so now?

 Walking in Wonder

I wonder…

👣 Walking Through Today: Journaling the Journey

_____

_____

_____

_____

_____

_____

_____

_____

_____

_____

_____

_____

_____

_____

_____

_____

_____

_____

_____

_____

_____

_____

_____

_____

_____

_____

_____

_____

_____

_____

_____

_____

_____

_____

_____

_____

_____

_____

_____

_____

_____

_____

Walking Through Today: Journaling the Journey   Date:_____

The Commission of the Church

Go therefore and make disciples of all the nations,
baptizing them in the name of the Father and the Son and the Holy Spirit
teaching them to observe all that I commanded you;
and lo, I am with you always, even to the end of the age.
Matthew 28:19-20

 ## Walking with Him through the Word

We live in an "it's all about me" world, but this is not so for the church, the believers in Christ. While we are *journeying with Jesus* as His body, housing His Spirit, and serving one another, He has commissioned us to a work in this world. Let's study the Word to discover this great work.

New Testament Scripture:

1. Please read Matthew 28:18-20. Who has all authority over heaven and earth? Who has commissioned us?

From these verses, list the instructions given the church, the body of believers.

What assurance is given to those who are commissioned?

<u>Why do you think it is key to know He is always with you as you go?</u>

The word, disciple, means "learner, pupil, to follow the precepts and instructions of another." **All believers are disciples – followers of Christ.**

As believers (disciples) we are to go out into the world to make other followers (or pupils) of Jesus. Baptism is a sign of identification with someone or something and points to the fact we are to make followers of Jesus Christ. The disciple is to identify with Christ, then, and not with the disciple who brings the message to him.

<u>What else is the believer/disciple to do besides go and make other disciples?</u>

<u>Where are all the command Christ taught found?</u>

<u>Is this commission for a pastor, preacher, or evangelist only?</u>
(see II Corinthians 5:19-20 for added help with your answer.)

2. <u>Now, read Matthew 5:13-16 please. (Don't get dizzy backing up in the Scriptures</u>.)
<u>How are believers described in these verses?</u> ·

<u>How, then, can disciples be the salt of the earth</u>?

<u>What does light do?</u>

<u>How, then, can disciples be the light of the world?</u>

3. <u>Finally, please read II Corinthians 2:14-16. How are believers/disciples described in</u> <u>verse 14?</u>

<u>According to verse 15, how are you described and how does He use you in His</u> <u>procession according to verse 14?</u>

<u>As a Christlike fragrance, what are the results of you being in the world (verse 16)?</u>

 ## Walking with Others

Did you realize you are commissioned by the Lord to be His disciple, taking the gospel message and all the Lord's good teaching to others? You are called to go, to be salt and light in your sphere of influence. As His disciple, God is using you in this world. Your life is the scent of the victory of your King. Some are attracted to Christ by the aroma of Christlikeness in your words and deeds. You are just like sweet perfume: intriguing, soothing, comforting. Others are repelled, for they reject Christ and so your sweetness annoys and sickens them. But you, captive disciple, are a sweet fragrance rising up to God as you are *journeying with Jesus* in His triumphal procession.

Walking in Prayer

Truth calls for response. Spend some time now in prayer, thanking God for who you are in Him – light, salt, an ambassador, and like sweet perfume rising up as a pleasing aroma to your King. Ask for His wisdom and guidance to be about His business – commissioned to share as His disciple.

Walking through the Psalms

Pease read and think about Psalm 96. How does the psalmist proclaim the good news of God? Do you not feel his excitement and joy? He loves to sing God's praises and declare Him to the world. Does it not inspire you to do the same?

Walking in Wonder

Don't forget to jot down any questions you might have, so we can cover them in class.

👣 Walking Through Today: Journaling the Journey

_____

_____

_____

_____

_____

_____

_____

_____

_____

_____

_____

_____

_____

_____

_____

_____

_____

_____

_____

_____

Walking Through Today: Journaling the Journey   Date:_____

Section C

Until Then

Week Seven

Sights Along the Way

Day One	Walk in Faith
Day Two	Walk in Obedience
Day Three	Walk in New Live
Day Four	Walk in Humility and Trust
Day Five	Walk in Joy and Endurance

Walk in Faith

Now faith is the assurance of things hoped for,
the conviction of things not seen.
Hebrews 11:1

 ## Walking with Him through the Word

Okay! We have a spiritual backpack filled with all we need to live godly lives as we are *journeying with Jesus*. This week, let's spend some time considering our walk. May I point out some sights of interest along the way? Grab your backpack and let's go!

In the Old Testament we are given many examples of people who walked with God. What can we learn from their walks?

Old Testament Scripture:

1. <u>Please read Genesis 5:21-24</u>. <u>How many years did Enoch live?</u>

<u>How many years did he walk with God?</u>

<u>Then, what happened to Enoch?</u>

2. <u>Please read Genesis 6:8-10</u>. <u>List all the things you discover about Noah from these verses.</u>

Both of these men are examples for us of the work of God called "sanctification," the act of God in setting apart a person from the world and to Himself. "Progressive sanctification" is the act of God in daily transforming a person from the inside out to become more and more like Jesus Christ, in the way they think, and in what they say and do. He causes His children to **desire** to walk with Him in love and obedience just as Christ did when He was on earth, and He **empowers** them to do so – to walk with Him as did Enoch and Noah.

Both of these men who walked with God are listed in the New Testament's "Hall of Faith" chapter, Hebrews 11. (Read the chapter to discover why it's been titled in such a way – a fun time of discovery!)

New Testament Scripture:

3. Please read Hebrews 11:5-7. According to verses 5 and 6, before Enoch was taken to heaven, what was known about him?

How are you like Enoch? What in your life reveals to the world around you that you please God, that you are a person of faith?

<u>What else did you learn about Noah's walk from verse.7?</u>

<u>How are your actions and words declaring faith in the Lord's good promises?</u>

 ## Walking with Others

Journeying with Jesus is always a walk of faith. It begins with belief (which is faith) and continues in belief. Both Enoch and Noah put their faith in the Word of God, believing His promises to the point of obedience to God. In doing so, they became witnesses to the world that God is real and He is a Promise Keeper. Both men became heirs of righteousness based on their faith. We'll meet them in eternity future. As a believer, you are an heir of righteousness like Enoch and Noah. Is your life a witness to those around you that you walk with God?

Walking in Prayer

Spend some time walking with God in prayer. Imagine He is holding your hand as you "pour out your heart like water" (Lamentation 2:19). Ask Him to help you make your witness clear so He is glorified by your life's journey.

Walking through the Psalms

Please read Psalm 23, perhaps aloud. As you are *journeying, with Jesus* as your Shepherd, how is your walk affected? List what you discover.

 Walking in Wonder

Any questions?

Walking Through Today: Journaling the Journey

Walking Through Today: Journaling the Journey   Date:_____

Walk in Obedience

You shall walk in all the way
which the LORD your God has commanded you,
that you may live and that it may be well with you...
Deuteronomy 5:33

Shall we take a walk through the Scriptures today? I'd like to explore the "how-tos" of our walk with God. How does God say we are to walk (daily lifestyle) as we are *journeying with Jesus* to our heavenly home? Today we'll stroll through the Old Testament and tomorrow the New Testament.

Walking with Him through the Word

Old Testament Scripture:

1. Please read Deuteronomy 5:33. What exhortation did God give through Moses to the Israelites, God's chosen people?

2. Please read Deuteronomy 28:9, 10. How does Moses confirm once again what God told the Israelites in Deuteronomy 5:33?

3. Read Joshua 22:5 and note how Joshua encouraged the Israelites to walk.

4. <u>Please read I Kings 2:1-3. How did King David exhort his son Solomon to walk as the next king of Israel?</u>

5. <u>Read Psalm 1:1. Note how God's people are NOT to walk (a negative to re-enforce a positive).</u>

6. <u>How are we to walk according to Proverbs 20:7?</u>

*This stroll has turned into quite a hike – hang in there–
just one more passage I want you to see.*

7. <u>Please read Isaiah 40:31. What wonderful principle is given for those who wait for the Lord?</u> (Waiting means to walk life's journey entwined with Him.)

Walking with Others

Strolling through the Old Testament, you discover the beautiful exhortations and encouragements to walk in obedience to all God commands. His way is the good, right way to journey. After all, He created you and He should know! The blessings of life are found through obedience. And through your obedience to His Word, you are walking in a deep, close, love relationship with One Who loves you so and created you to walk closely with Him. When you do, your walk becomes a witness of the great love God has for His own and shows His desire to share that love with all who will come to Him.

Don't forget the awesome provision of His Holy Spirit who enables and empowers you to obey! As you yield to obey, by His great power, He conforms you into the image of your Lord. He lived a life of obedience while on earth, as an example for you. What a win-win situation you find yourself in.

Walking in Prayer

As you think about the rich blessing of obedience, won't you pray in thanksgiving and praise to your Father for the clear and simple (though not always easy) path of life He has given you? Ask the Lord to reveal any areas of disobedience so you can confess and repent, be cleansed, and enjoy the sweet fellowship of your *journey with Jesus* (see 1 John 1:9).

Walking through the Psalms

Read and meditate (ponder, think about) Psalm 30. How do you see the blessings of obedience in this Psalm?

 Walking in Wonder

???

Walking Through Today: Journaling the Journey

_____

_____

_____

_____

_____

_____

_____

_____

_____

_____

_____

_____

_____

_____

_____

_____

_____

_____

_____

_____

Walking Through Today: Journaling the Journey   Date:_____

Walk in New Life

*Therefore we have been buried with Him through baptism into death,
so that as Christ was raised from the dead through the glory of the Father,
so we too might walk in newness of life.*
Romans 6:4

 ## Walking with Him through the Word

Do you have your hiking boots on and your backpack of provisions at hand? Let's hike (stroll is NOT the word for what we do – we HIKE!) through the New Testament to see how you are to walk as you are *journeying with Jesus.*

New Testament Scripture:

1. <u>Please read Romans 6:4.</u> <u>Because you belong to Christ, what privilege are you given?</u>

2. <u>How do you walk according to 2 Corinthians 5:7?</u>

As believers, we are now spiritually alive with a new biblical perspective. We see live through the eyes of faith in Jesus Christ and His Word.

3. <u>Read Ephesians 2:10.</u> <u>As created anew in Christ, how are you described and what is your purpose?</u>

4. According to Ephesians 5:2, how are you to walk? Who is your example, and how did He make it possible for you follow His example?

5. Please read Ephesians 5:8-9. What contrast is given and how are we to walk?

Are you out of breath?
Keep going – you are strengthening your spiritual muscles!

6. How are you told to walk in Colossians 2:6-7, and how are you empowered to do it?

7. If the blood of Jesus Christ has cleansed you from all sin, how will you walk according to I John 1:7?

8. <u>In Revelation 3:4, Christ commends some in the church</u>. <u>What did He say they did and what will be their reward?</u>

Good job! You've reached the summit! Isn't the view fantastic!
Hope you enjoyed the hike!

 ## Walking with Others

What a life you've been given! Christ Jesus your Lord has provided you with a new life, a new way of walking. No longer do you walk in the darkness of sin and its power. Now, you walk in the light of the Lord. He has opened your spiritual eyes to see how wonderful it is to live His way, according to His good Word. God even calls you His "masterpiece" and declares you were part of His plan all along! As you walk in obedience, by His power, you are walking in His good plan. You can know, as you walk now in obedience and fellowship with Him and one another in the body, God is doing His great work of sanctification in your life, making you like Jesus. You can walk now in holiness as you look forward to your journey's end when you'll be truly without any stain of sin, walking in white with your beloved Bridegroom.

Walking in Prayer

The Lord has spoken to you through His Word and now you can respond to Him through prayer. How can you respond to what you've just studied?

Walking through the Psalms

Please take a stroll through Psalm 112. How do you see the blessings of walking with the Lord from this passage?

 Walking in Wonder

Any questions??

Walking Through Today: Journaling the Journey

_____

_____

_____

_____

_____

_____

_____

_____

_____

_____

_____

_____

_____

_____

_____

_____

_____

_____

_____

_____

Journeying With Jesus Through the Basics

Walking Through Today: Journaling the Journey

Date:_____

Walk in Humility and Trust

Those who are left will be the lowly and humble
for it is they who trust in the name of the Lord.
Zephaniah 3:12 (NLT)

 ## Walking with Him through the Word

Journeying with Jesus is such a grand adventure!! It's the only way to truly live! As you've hiked through the Scriptures, you've been excited about the joy it is to be His and to walk with Him. But what happens when you stumble – when you fall into sin? What can you do? Is there any hope? And what do you do when you don't know what to do – when you are in an impossible situation? Is there any instruction? Let's once again hike through the Word and I'll show you some sights, so you'll gain "insight" to help you along the way.

Old Testament Scripture:

1. Read II Chronicles 7:14. What were the Israelites told to do when they had failed to walk in obedience? What would be the results?

Though this promise was made specifically to Israel, there are certain corresponding promises made to the church in the New Testament.

New Testament Scripture:

2. Please read James 4:6-10. What aspects of the instructions to Israel do you see in this passage to the church?

3. How have you appropriated these instructions when you have sinned? What have been the results?

Old Testament Scripture:

4. Please read Isaiah 50:10-11. What instruction is given to the believer who is in an impossible situation (not walking in sin – just a bad circumstance) as described in verse10?

What warning is also given in verse 11?

New Testament Scripture:

5. Read James 1:2-8, a parallel passage to the above Old Testament passage. What is your heart attitude to be toward impossible situations?

What is the purpose of the impossible situation according to verse 3 and 4?

What specifically are you to do in the impossible situation?

And what does God promise to do?

What is the condition for His giving you wisdom to know how to deal with the situation?

If you waver, what does this reveal about your heart?

If you waver, will you receive the wisdom you need?

How can you know if you are walking in humility and trust? What can you do to be sure? Let's continue to hike through our Father's good Word to find out.

Old Testament Scripture:

6. <u>According to Psalm 139:23-24, what are you called to do?</u>

New Testament Scripture:

7. <u>According to Matthew 7:5 and I Corinthians 11:31, what are you called to do?</u>

8. <u>Finally, read Jude 24 and write out the promise – word for word</u>. <u>This is your hope and mine</u>.

9. <u>In your struggle against sin or in your impossible situation, how can examining yourself make a difference in your response?</u>

Walking with Others

God, your Father, has given you definite direction for the problem of falling in sin and for the impossible circumstances of life. A life of humility and trust. All sin reveals a heart of pride from which repentance in humility leads to cleansing. All impossible circumstances give opportunity to reveal a heart of trust in the God who declares, "Nothing is impossible with God" (Luke 1:37). Through prayer and knowing the Word of God, you can examine yourself before the omniscient, gracious Father to receive cleansing if needed, or wisdom to trust and act according to His good will in the circumstance. The adventure continues as He does His sanctifying work in your life, walking you home to heaven.

The Road of Life

At first I saw God as my observer, my judge,
keeping track of the things I did wrong,
so as to know whether I merited heaven or hell when I die.
He was out there sort of like a president.
I recognized His picture when I saw it,
but I really didn't know Him.

But later on when I met Christ,
It seemed as though life were rather like a bike ride,
but it was a tandem bike,
and I noticed that Christ
was in the back helping me pedal.

I don't know just when it was
that He suggested we change places,
but life has not been the same since.

When I had control, I knew the way.
It was rather boring, but predictable....
It was the shortest distance between two points.

But when He took the lead, He knew delightful long cuts,
up mountains, and through rocky places
at breakneck speeds,
it was all I could do to hang on!
Even though it looked like madness,
He said, *Pedal!*

I worried and was anxious and asked,
Where are you taking me?
He laughed and didn't answer,
and I started to learn to trust.

I forgot my boring life
and entered into the adventure.
And when I'd say, *I'm scared,*
He'd lean back and touch my hand.

He took me to people with gifts that I needed,
gifts of healing, acceptance, and joy.
They gave me gifts to take on my journey,
my Lord's and mine.

And we were off again.
He said, *Give the gifts away;*
they're extra baggage, too much weight.
So I did, to the people we met,
and I found that in giving I received,
and still our burden was light.

I did not trust Him, at first, in control of my life.
I thought He'd wreck it; but He knows bike secrets,
knows how to make it bend to take sharp corners,
knows how to jump to clear high rocks,
knows how to fly to shorten scary passages.

And I am learning to be quiet
and pedal in the strangest places,
and I'm beginning to enjoy the view
and the cool breeze on my face
with my delightful constant companion, Jesus Christ.

And when I'm sure I just can't do any more,
He just smiles and says…*Pedal.*

--Author Unknown—

Walking in Prayer

Please spend some time in prayer examining yourself before God. If cleansing for sin is needed, as He reveals your heart to you, humble yourself in confession. If wisdom is needed for an impossible circumstance, ask Him in faith -- with thanksgiving in your heart and on your lips -- trusting His answer and timing. You may use the space below to record your prayer.

Walking through the Psalms

The psalmist writes of God's sanctifying work in the lives of His children in Psalm 40. Spend some time reading and reflecting on what you see there. How do you see God's cleansing for sin and its results? How does He explain the joy of trusting God?

Walking in Wonder

Do you have any questions?

Walking Through Today: Journaling the Journey

Walking Through Today: Journaling the Journey   Date:_____

WALKING IN FAITHFULNESS

*He who is faithful in a very little thing
is faithful also in much...*
Luke 16:10

 Walking with Him through the Word

When I picked up my son from junior high school (many, many years ago!), anxious to hear about his day, I asked, "How was your day, Drew?" His reply was "boring." Since I didn't like the word or its connotation, I asked him not to answer that way. The next day when I asked about his day, he responded with a new answer, "daily." I learned to ask about his day in a new way after that, but his "daily" reply has become a family joke and standard reply to a day without significant events.

If there is anything life is, it's "daily." Up in the morning...routine and responsibilities...and down at night. If you are young, you have the r & r (routine and responsibilities) of school. If you have young children, it's the r & r of nurturing and training them. If you have no children or if you are 'older' with no children left in the home, it's the r & r of running the home and serving others. See, it's "daily." How can we walk in the "dailies" in such a way that God will be both pleased and glorified?

Old Testament Scripture:

1. <u>Please read Ecclesiastes 1:3-4. What question did Solomon, the Preacher, ask in verse 3?</u>

<u>How does he view the "dailies" of life in verse 4?</u>

Solomon, the wisest man on the earth during his lifetime, posed a question as to the purpose of life with its seeming futility of living in the "dailies." What is the purpose of the "dailies?" Is there any plan to fulfill? Is there any point to the day-to-day routine of life? He then spent the rest of the book answering his own question. *And I set my mind to seek and explore by wisdom concerning all that has been done under heaven...* (Ecclesiastes 1:13).

2. Please read Ecclesiastes 2:24-25 to note Solomon's conclusion. What is God's intent for the "dailies," the r & r s of life?

He is saying the child of God is to find contentment, peace, and joy in the daily routines and responsibilities of life. Life – walking with God – is to be a grand adventure each and every moment of each and every day.

3. According to Ecclesiastes 3:12-13, what are the gifts of God to His children?

Your daily routine is a gift from God to enjoy! Are you enjoying it?

4. What reminder is given in Ecclesiastes 3:17?

The reminder is: what is done in the "dailies" counts! Since there is a time of judgment, enjoy each day by walking with Him. Since you are on the path of righteousness, live a righteous life of peace and joy in obedience to Him. Live with eternity in mind!

New Testament Scripture:

5. <u>Please read Matthew 5:14-16.</u> <u>How are you to live each day and for what reason?</u>

6. <u>Please read Luke 16:10 in the NASB (printed below).</u> <u>According to this verse, as we are faithful in little (the "dailies") God points out that we are also what?</u>

*"He who is faithful in a very little thing is faithful also in much;
and he who is unrighteous in a very little thing is unrighteous also in much.*

Faithfulness in your day-in-day-out routines and responsibilities (the little things) is considered by God as faithfulness "in much!" What is God's concern – His emphasis? The emphasis is on your faithfulness, not on the seeming size of the work. The smallest task of life is considered by God as huge if it is done in faithfulness to Him.

7. <u>According to John 10: 10, why did Jesus say He came?</u>

*Once again, I have you hiking through the Word. How are you doing?
Can you go a little further? It will be worth it, my friend.*

8. <u>What is the purpose of the "dailies" according to Romans 8:28-29?</u>

9. Please read Philippians 4:11-12. What secret had Paul learned about living in the "dailies?"

10. Please read Colossians 3:17, 23-24. According to verses 17 and 23, how are you to go about the routines & responsibilities (the r & r's) of your life?

According to verse 24, whom do you serve as you walk faithfully in the "dailies?"

Also, according to verse 24, what are you to consider as you walk?

11. According to what you have seen in today's lesson, how are you to view your day-to-day life?

12. How does your faithfulness in the "dailies" show love to God and to others?

13. What changes can you make today to insure your life brings glory to the Lord in the "dailies?"

 ## Walking with Others

Jesus came to give you life – a rich and satisfying life! What a gift! All of our life is a good gift from His hand. He wants you to enjoy your life – all of it. With the ups and the downs, the ins and the outs, its routines and responsibilities (the "dailies"). He calls every part of your day a gift from His hand to enjoy. Life isn't about waiting for some huge event or circumstance to prove yourself faithful to God. He calls you to be faithful in the "dailies" and, as you are, He judges you faithful. And those acts of faithfulness have eternal value – as much eternal value as any "big thing" – for they prove you are His beloved and they show Him faithful.

Are you enjoying your life? Are you finding contentment in the "dailies?" Or are you anxiously waiting for God to bring some big, exciting event into your life so you can prove to the world you are a worthy child? Every moment of your life is a gift from God, and you can give Him the gift of faithfulness in return. As you do, you will discover the secret of contentment, as did Paul. And your life, every moment, will be a testimony to the world of the great goodness of God. He will be glorified through the "dailies" your life!

Walking in Prayer

Do you need to learn contentment, to enjoy "the dailies?" Do you long to live a life that glorifies your Lord? These two things go hand in hand, don't they? Won't you pray today and ask God to reveal anything you need to know and do to learn the secret of contentment? And won't you, then, yield to the Holy Spirit's control of your life, so you are walking in the Spirit, in the love, joy, peace that is yours in Him?

Write out your prayer to help you articulate your thoughts and remember your prayer.

Walking through the Psalms

Read aloud Psalm 131. How do you see the contentment of the psalmist in this psalm? May I encourage you to memorize this psalm, for it is a good reminder to be content and enjoy the "dailies," and so honor your God?

Walking in Wonder

Don't forget to write out any questions you might have from today's lesson.

Walking Through Today: Journaling the Journey

_____

_____

_____

_____

_____

_____

_____

_____

_____

_____

_____

_____

_____

_____

_____

_____

_____

_____

_____

_____

_____

_____

Walking Through Today: Journaling the Journey

Date:_____

Week Eight

Journey's End – Jesus face-to-Face

Day One   The Place of Eternity Future

Day Two   The City and Kingdom of Eternity Future

Day Three   The Purity of Heaven – Eternity Future

Day Four   The Vista View of Eternity Future

Day Five   The Risen Lord of Eternity Future

The Place of Eternity Future

"Do not let your heart be troubled; believe in God, believe also in Me.
"In My Father's house are many dwelling places; if it were not so, I would have told you;
for I go to prepare a place for you. "If I go and prepare a place for you,
I will come again and receive you to Myself, that where I am, there you may be also.
John 14:1-3

 ## Walking with Him through the Word

Thinking about heaven is absolutely heavenly. It is exciting and comforting to think about your final destination. And, you know, as you sojourn here on this earth, you are in the process of *journeying with Jesus* to paradise. Living with eternity in mind includes the joyful expectation of heaven.

Some people don't like to think about heaven, because they don't know what to expect or are afraid of having to die to get there. Let's remove the fear by knowing some of the basic truths about heaven, eternity future.

1. In the Bible, the term heaven is used in three ways. Please read the following verses, noting the word 'heaven'. Record what you learn about the place referred to as heaven in each of these passages.

Old Testament Scripture:

Genesis 1:7-8, 20

Genesis 1:14-15

New Testament Scripture:

II Corinthians 12:2-4 (also underline a synonym used for heaven found in this passage.)

387

2. In Luke 23:43, when Jesus was crucified and the robber beside Him confessed his faith in Jesus, what promise did Jesus make to him?

3. According to John 14:1-3, what does Jesus tell us about this eternal place and what does He promise us?

Heaven is a real, definitive place. It is the Father's house where the Lord has gone to prepare a place for us as His redeemed. It's not an idea, an image, a state of nirvana. It is a place and because we are the Lord's, we will go there.

Old Testament Scripture:

4. Read Isaiah 6:1-4. List what you learn about heaven from Isaiah's vision.

New Testament Scripture:

5. Please read Revelation 4:2-8 and list what you learn about heaven from John's vision of God's throne.

6.   <u>Read Revelation 5:6, 11-12.</u>   <u>Who is between the throne and the four living creatures and what is the response in heaven to Him?</u>

7. <u>From today's passages, what is your favorite discovery about this place called heaven?</u>

 ## Walking with Others

Heaven, where we'll spend eternity future, is a real, definite place – the glorious place where God lives, high and seated on His throne. It is a place so grand, it is almost indescribable and too marvelous for words, but we have been given glimpses – like snapshots- to reflect upon with wonder and hope until Jesus returns for us and walks us safely through heaven's door and we are home.

Walking in Prayer

As you have spent some time reflecting upon the place of eternity and the visions of Isaiah and John, aren't you filled with awe and wonder? As you realize the Lord Jesus Christ has prepared a place in heaven just for you, are you not overcome with praise? How can you respond in prayer to these incredible truths? Write out your prayer response, please.

Walking through the Psalms

Please read and meditate on Psalm 99 today. What do you learn about the wonders of heaven and the God of heaven from this psalm?

Walking in Wonder

????????????????????????????????

Walking Through Today: Journaling the Journey

_____

_____

_____

_____

_____

_____

_____

_____

_____

_____

_____

_____

_____

_____

_____

_____

_____

_____

_____

_____

Walking Through Today: Journaling the Journey   Date:_____

The City and Kingdom of Eternity Future

But as it is, they desire a better country, that is, a heavenly one.
Therefore God is not ashamed to be called their God;
for He has prepared a city for them.
Hebrews 11:16

Walking with Him through the Word

Hebrews 11 is filled with the names of believers who lived with eternity in mind! They understood a great truth: heaven was their true homeland, their true country. So they *journeyed with Jesus* through thick and thin, devoting themselves to their King and their homeland - the Kingdom of Heaven. What truths about heaven did they understand that caused them to live by faith and walk with confident determination toward home? Let's look and see.

New Testament Scripture:

1. <u>Please read Hebrews 11:10-16.</u>   <u>For what was Abraham confidently looking according to verse 10?</u>

<u>According to verses 13-16, what was the mind-set of all these men and women of faith listed in Hebrews 11?</u> <u>For what were they all looking forward?</u>

<u>Write out word for word Hebrews 11:16.</u>

Again, where were the believer's sights set?

What has God prepared for the believer, proving He is delighted to be called their God?

2. Please read Hebrews 12:22-24, noticing the word "come" in your Bible. To what has the believer come?

3. Hebrews 13:14 in the NASB reads: *"For here we do not have a lasting city, but we are seeking the city which is to come."* What is the city we are seeking?

Keep up the good work! There's so much too see! Can you go a little further?
The next hike is a "doozie" but well worth the sight.

4. <u>Revelation 21:1-7;10-21, and 22:1-3 is written out below for you.</u> <u>Underline the key descriptions of the beloved city that capture your heart.</u>

1 Then I saw a new heaven and a new earth, for the old heaven and the old earth had disappeared. And the sea was also gone. 2 And I saw the holy city, the new Jerusalem, coming down from God out of heaven like a bride beautifully dressed for her husband.
3 I heard a loud shout from the throne, saying, "Look, God's home is now among his people! He will live with them, and they will be his people. God himself will be with them. 4 He will wipe every tear from their eyes, and there will be no more death or sorrow or crying or pain. All these things are gone forever."
5 And the one sitting on the throne said, "Look, I am making everything new!" And then he said to me, "Write this down, for what I tell you is trustworthy and true." 6 And he also said, "It is finished! I am the Alpha and the Omega—the Beginning and the End. To all who are thirsty I will give freely from the springs of the water of life. 7 All who are victorious will inherit all these blessings, and I will be their God, and they will be my children.

10 So he took me in the Spirit to a great, high mountain, and he showed me the holy city, Jerusalem, descending out of heaven from God. 11 It shone with the glory of God and sparkled like a precious stone—like jasper as clear as crystal. 12 The city wall was broad and high, with twelve gates guarded by twelve angels. And the names of the twelve tribes of Israel were written on the gates. 13 There were three gates on each side—east, north, south, and west. 14 The wall of the city had twelve foundation stones, and on them were written the names of the twelve apostles of the Lamb.
15 The angel who talked to me held in his hand a gold measuring stick to measure the city, its gates, and its wall. 16 When he measured it, he found it was a square, as wide as it was long. In fact, its length and width and height were each 1,400 miles. 17 Then he measured the walls and found them to be 216 feet thick (according to the human standard used by the angel).
18 The wall was made of jasper, and the city was pure gold, as clear as glass. 19 The wall of the city was built on foundation stones inlaid with twelve precious stones: the first was jasper, the second sapphire, the third agate, the fourth emerald, 20 the fifth onyx, the sixth carnelian, the seventh chrysolite, the eighth beryl, the ninth topaz, the tenth chrysoprase, the eleventh jacinth, the twelfth amethyst.
21 The twelve gates were made of pearls—each gate from a single pearl! And the main street was pure gold, as clear as glass.

1 Then the angel showed me a river with the water of life, clear as crystal, flowing from the throne of God and of the Lamb. 2 It flowed down the center of the main street. On each side of the river grew a tree of life, bearing twelve crops of fruit, with a fresh crop each month. The leaves were used for medicine to heal the nations.
3 No longer will there be a curse upon anything. For the throne of God and of the Lamb will be there, and his servants will worship him.

5. How do you know for sure you are a citizen of this city?

6. What kind of life will you have as a citizen of this beloved city?

Walking with Others

The city of God is a holy city in a holy kingdom, prepared by our holy God just for His holy children. The Lord Jesus Christ has prepared it perfectly and has secured our citizenship by His blood sacrifice (this is called the New Covenant of grace). It is a grand and glorious city – beautiful beyond description, as is our Lord the King. As citizens, we will live in "the lap of luxury," the lap of our God. His glory will illumine our lives and all will be well. We will behold His face and dwell in His presence for eternity! Just these few glimpses of the eternal city call us home, fill our hearts with longing, and make Paul's statement in Philippians 3:20 one of the most profound ever expressed. *For our citizenship is in heaven, from which also we eagerly wait for a Savior, the Lord Jesus Christ.*

Walking in Prayer

Take one of the passages you have just studied, one that spoke to your heart, as a springboard to pray. Ask God to make you more and more like the Hebrews 11 saints, a person who looks to the heavenly city and lives with eternity in mind.

Walking through the Psalms

How does Psalm 125 speak to your citizenship in heaven? What promises do you see?

 ## Walking in Wonder

Do you have any questions? Don't forget to jot them down.

Walking Through Today: Journaling the Journey

_____

_____

_____

_____

_____

_____

_____

_____

_____

_____

_____

_____

_____

_____

_____

_____

_____

_____

_____

_____

_____

_____

_____

Walking Through Today: Journaling the Journey   Date:_____

The Purity of Heaven – Eternity Future

and nothing unclean, and no one who practices abomination and lying,
shall ever come into it, but only those whose names
are written in the Lamb's book of life.
Revelation 21:27

 ## Walking with Him through the Word

Recently we were driving in California freeway traffic. We were in what is called "stop and go" mode which was mostly "stop." People were weaving in and out just trying to move a car-length further. The driver was worn out from having to be hyper-vigilant. Others in the car were cheering him on, praying for "traveling mercies." As we were sitting in the middle of this mess, I wondered to the Lord, "What are You trying to teach each one of us, driver and passengers, in this traffic situation?" Patience, certainly, along with trust and endurance. Then, it dawned on me – THERE"LL BE NO TRAFFIC IN HEAVEN! Yea!! (I'm a very deep thinker, you can tell.) And even if there was, we wouldn't care! No! – no traffic in heaven. What other things, I continued to ponder, won't be in heaven to irritate our oh, so sensitive nerves – cranky people, failed recipes, charge cards (well, not the cards but the bills), scratched c.d.s, flat tires, broken appliances, people being late the one time you aren't, changing wardrobe sizes – need I go on? The Bible tells us about some things that won't be in heaven we can add to that list. Look up the following Scriptures to see what will not be there.

New Testament Scripture:

1. Please read Philippians 3:20-21. What is Jesus going to change?

2. Please read I Corinthians 15:42-49. According to this passage, what kind of body will believers have in heaven? What will they be like?

Yes, in heaven, there will be no more earthly bodies that get sick and die. We'll have spiritual bodies like our Lord.

3. Please read Romans 8:18-25. According to verses 21 and 23, what do believers long for and look forward to even though we have the Holy Spirit indwelling us now?

All pain and suffering in the world is due to sin. Believers long for the time there will be no more sin and no more grief over sin. For there will be no sin in heaven, so no one will sin in heaven!

How does knowing your struggle against sin will end help you now (see verses 24 and 25 to help you answer)?

4. <u>Please turn to Revelation</u>. <u>According to the following passages, what else will not be in heaven?</u>

<u>Revelation 20:10</u>

<u>Revelation 20:14-15</u>

<u>Revelation 21:1</u>

<u>Revelation 21:8</u>

<u>Revelation 21:22-27</u>

<u>Revelation 22:3, 5,15</u>

 ## Walking with Others

Just think of the purity of heaven – of eternity future. No sin, sinful desires, temptations to sin, or reminders of sin. You will have a new, glorified body, fit to live in the heavenly atmosphere, fit to love and serve the Lord perfectly and fully. There will certainly be nothing to irritate. And speaking of that, there is no reason for the things of earth to irritate you or me now. We are God's and He is in complete control. All the "irritations" are purposeful in His good hands. As a child of God, all of life has purpose – every enjoyment and every irritation. As we recognize this truth, situations become, instead of an irritation, simply another occasion to love, trust, and rely on our Lord. It's another opportunity to praise Him in all things until our journey's end in heaven, where we'll praise Him face-to-Face forever.

Walking in Prayer

As you've seen the purity of our full redemptive state in heaven, how can you respond in prayer? Is your heart filled with praise and thanksgiving? Are there irritations in your life you need to "cast on Him for He cares for you?" (1 Peter 5:7)   Pour out your heart before Him now.

Walking through the Psalms

Read purposefully Psalm 121. Notice where your help comes from and list all He does for you. Spend some time meditating on these promises. You might want to personalize them. (For instance: I thank You, Father, for You will not allow my foot to slip. You are watching over my life to keep me faithful.)

Walking in Wonder
Any questions today?

Walking Through Today: Journaling the Journey

_____

_____

_____

_____

_____

_____

_____

_____

_____

_____

_____

_____

_____

_____

_____

_____

_____

_____

_____

_____

Walking Through Today: Journaling the Journey   Date:_____

The Vista View of Eternity Future

He who loves his life loses it,
and he who hates his life in this world
will keep it to life eternal.
John 12:25

 ## Walking with Him through the Word

Recently we bought our "retirement property," four beautiful acres in Texas with a vista view of the Guadalupe River winding through a huge meadow, silhouetted by the Texas hills. It's grand. Grander still are the vista views from the peaks of the Colorado Rockies. Vista views can take your breath away by their beauty.

God also has a vista view – and it's a vista view of eternity. It is the grandest of views! And He has shared it with us in His Word – eternity past to eternity future. From eternity past, God Almighty planned for the believer's eternity future. He calls it *eternal life.* And His Son, Jesus Christ, died to secure our possession of it and He ever lives making intercession for us now at the right-hand of the Father until His prayer for us is realized and we are where He is (see John 17:24). Today, let's enjoy a vista view of *eternal life.*

New Testament Scripture:

1. <u>Please read John 3:14-16</u>. <u>What did Jesus promise the one who puts his faith in Christ?</u>

2. <u>According to John 5:28-29, what destination is clearly noted for every person ever born?</u>

3. Please read John 11:23-27. What glorious revelation of Himself did Jesus proclaim to Martha?

How did Jesus explain what the impact would be for a person who believed Him to be the Resurrection and the Life?

What was Martha's response?

4. According to John 12:25, what is the ultimate result of giving one's life to Christ?

Eternal life is Christ's term for heaven, where we will live in His presence forever!

5. Write out John 17:23-24 (Christ's prayer for your eternal life with Him) as a reminder.

6. <u>According to the following verses, what things in heaven are described using the word "life?"</u>

<u>James 1:12</u>

<u>Revelation 7:17</u>

<u>Revelation 13:8</u>

<u>Revelation 22:1</u>

<u>Revelation 22:2</u>

7. <u>Please read 1 Timothy 6:12</u>. <u>As Paul exhorted Timothy, how are you exhorted</u> <u>concerning eternal life</u>?

 ## Walking with Others

We grieve at the thought of leaving earth and family through death, because we don't want to miss the celebrations of this life. How do you change your focus - hold tightly to eternal life? You do it by gazing intently at the vista view of heaven, the celebrations of the eternal life. The qualities of the divine life – the intimacy of being in the Lamb's Book of Life, the refreshment and satisfaction of the rivers of living water, the healing and abundant blessing of the tree of life - can fill your soul with joy and peace now as you are *journeying with Jesus* to heaven, your true home. As you journey in intimacy with Him and grow in your relationship with Christ, heaven will grow dearer. As you live heart–to–Heart with Him now, you will grasp more and more the life you will enjoy face–to–Face in eternity future. Let's hold tightly. Hold tightly!

~~~~~~~~~~~~~~~~~~~~~~~~~~~~~~~~~~~~~~~

But eternal life involves the untold, unimagined, and fadeless glories of heaven! What measureless wealth! What deathless raptures! What glorious intoxication! No description dare attempt its picture. The most exalted strains of music would be discord to the harmony of heaven, and the brightest vision would turn to darkest midnight! All summer suns would chill like the ice of December when contrasted with the splendor of heaven's nightless day. The most gifted, exalted, and sweetest poetry of earth would be but dull prose in heaven.

What is eternal life? Who can dream or imagine that life? Heaven has it! Heaven holds it! It will be the surprise of the saints as they leave earth and pass through the gates of the Celestial City.

E.M. Bounds in *A Place Called Heaven* [13]

Walking in Prayer

You might want to spend some time reading Jesus' prayer for His disciples recorded in John 17. Listen for His heart as He prayed. Then, won't you consider asking God to give you a heart for heaven? Ask the Lord to increase your understanding of the qualities of eternal life through the snapshots He's given you in His Word. (Listening to His Word and responding in prayer is heart-to-Heart time with the Lord.)

Walking through the Psalms

Please read and meditate on Psalm 136 today. How do you see the vista view of God's love and eternal plan in this psalm?

 Walking in Wonder

Questions Anyone?

Walking Through Today: Journaling the Journey

_____

_____

_____

_____

_____

_____

_____

_____

_____

_____

_____

_____

_____

_____

_____

_____

_____

_____

_____

_____

_____

Walking Through Today: Journaling the Journey

Date:_____

The Risen Lord of Eternity Future

I am the first and the last, and the living One;
and I was dead, and behold,
I am alive forevermore...
Revelation 1:17b-18

 Walking with Him through the Word

The Bible has given some beautiful snapshots of heaven – glimpses into eternity future. You've seen the place, city, kingdom of heaven of which believers are citizens. You'll go there with new, pure, holy, glorified bodies perfectly fit for heavenly living. It is truly an eternal life of love, joy, and freedom from sin and death. Above all these beautiful picture truths, there is one more beautiful, more glorious picture still.

New Testament Scripture:

1. <u>Please read chapter 1 of Revelation. According to verse 1, this is the revelation of Whom?</u>

The word, revelation, means "to uncover or reveal." Just as the gospels revealed Jesus Christ's first coming – His humbling Himself to die on the cross, and His resurrection – the book of Revelation reveals the exaltation of Jesus Christ as the Risen Lord, in heaven now, but soon coming again in all His glory.

<u>On the chart at the end of today's lesson, list the revelation (description) of Christ given in verse 5.</u>

What reminder is given in verse 7?

Jesus Christ is coming to earth again. Just as the disciples saw Him ascend into heaven with the clouds, He will return the same way, as promised in the Old Testament book of Daniel (see 7:13) and in the New Testament book of Acts (see 1:11). The first time Jesus came to earth only a select few saw Him and recognized His deity. This time, He will come in all His glory, so every eye will see Him as God Almighty.

Please add to your chart, the further description of Christ given in verse 8.

Beginning in verse 9, the vision given to John is introduced. John turns at the sound of a voice instructing him to write what he sees and send it to the churches. Beginning in verse 13, we see his vision of the risen, glorified Lord Jesus Christ.

Continue to list on your chart how you see Jesus described in verses 13 through 16.

<u>According to verses 17-18, what was John's response?</u>

<u>What did Jesus reveal about Himself to comfort John (verse 18)?</u>

<u>Please read and note from verse 19, John's three-fold assignment.</u>

The book of Revelation can easily be outlined according to this verse. The vision of the Risen Lord Jesus Christ, which John had just seen was the first assignment. *The things which are* were written to the churches in existence at the time of the writing and are recorded in chapters 2 and 3. And *the things which shall take place after these things* comprise the rest of the book of Revelation. John obeyed Jesus, of course (see Revelation 1:2).

2.   <u>Now, please re-read the chapter to discover everything you can about the believers, the church. List these things on your chart under the column entitled "Believers."</u> (<u>I'll get you started</u>.)

verse 1 this revelation was written to show His servants (believers are Christ's servants) what must soon take place
verse 3 blessings are promised to the one who reads, listens to, and obeys what it says (believers would follow through to obedience).

Keep up the good work. I know this is quite a hike through Scripture, but you are strong from all the hikes we've taken thus far. You can do it! I just have a couple more awesome snapshots to show you before we complete our "Basics" course.

3. Please read Revelation 19:11-16. List all you learn about **the Risen Lord** on your chart. (This description comes at the time of Christ's Second Coming to earth to establish His kingdom. This is the culmination of all things and occurs at the end of the Tribulation period and before the Thousand Year reign of Christ on the earth. After this time, the new heaven and new earth will be created – called the Eternal State, for it will be forever and ever.)

List also on your chart, what you discover about **the believers** from this passage.

4. Please read Revelation 22:13-21. According to verses 13 and 16, how does Jesus describe Himself to confirm the validity of all the words of the prophesy? (Add this to your chart.)

What final invitation is given to those who want eternal life, and by whom is the invitation issued in verse 17?

What promise does Jesus leave us with as an encouragement and exhortation (verse 20)?

Is your response the same as the apostle John's – "Come, Lord Jesus?" Are you looking forward to His glorious return, when He will right every wrong and you will rule and reign with Him for a thousand years? When you will then live eternally in the eternal state of a new heaven and a new earth, where all will be pure and holy forever? *Amen! Come, Lord Jesus!*

Walking with Others

What an incredible picture of your Risen Lord in all His glory! He is no longer in a manger, no longer on a cross, but glorified at the Father's right hand! You will one day be in His Presence, face-to-Face, glorified and conformed to His image. Until then, as you are watching and waiting for Him, what are you to do and what should you remember? II Peter 3:14-18 tells us:

Therefore, beloved, since you look for these things, be diligent to be found by Him in peace, spotless and blameless, and regard the patience of our Lord as salvation; just as also our beloved brother Paul, according to the wisdom given him, wrote to you, as also in all his letters, speaking in them of these things, in which are some things hard to understand, which the untaught and unstable distort, as they do also the rest of the Scriptures, to their own destruction. You therefore, beloved, knowing this beforehand, be on your guard so that you are not carried away by the error of unprincipled men and fall from your own steadfastness, but grow in the grace and knowledge of our Lord and Savior Jesus Christ. To Him be the glory, both now and to the day of eternity. Amen.

~~~~~~

"There is laid up for me a crown of righteousness." 2Timothy 4:8

Doubting one! thou hast often said, "I fear I shall never enter heaven." Fear not! all the people of God shall enter there. I love the quaint saying of a dying man, who exclaimed, "I have no fear of going home; I have sent all before me; God's finger is on the latch of my door, and I am ready for him to enter." "But," said one, "are you not afraid lest you should miss your inheritance?" "Nay," said he, "nay; there is one crown in heaven which the angel Gabriel could not wear, it will fit no head but mine. There is one throne in heaven which Paul the apostle could not fill; it was made for me, and I shall have it." O Christian, what a joyous thought! thy portion is secure; "there remaineth a rest." "But cannot I forfeit it?" No, it is entailed. If I be a child of God I shall not lose it. It is mine as securely as if I were there. Come with me, believer, and let us sit upon the top of Nebo, and view the goodly land, even Canaan. Seest thou that little river of death glistening in the sunlight, and across it dost thou see the pinnacles of the eternal city? Dost thou mark the pleasant country, and all its joyous inhabitants? Know, then, that if thou couldst fly across thou wouldst see written upon one of its many mansions, "This remaineth for such a one; preserved for him only. He shall be caught up to dwell for ever with God." Poor doubting one, see the fair inheritance; it is thine. If thou believest in the Lord Jesus, if thou hast repented of sin, if thou hast been renewed in heart, thou art one of the Lord's people, and there is a place reserved for thee, a crown laid up for thee, a harp specially provided for thee. No one else shall have thy portion, it is reserved in heaven for thee, and thou shalt have it ere long, for there shall be no vacant thrones in glory when all the chosen are gathered in.

Charles Haddon Spurgeon in *Morning and Evening* [14]

Walking in Prayer

What a wonderful way to end these weeks of study and prayer – with hearts turned toward home and toward the Lord of Eternity. Using the list you made, spend some time with the Lord in praise and thanksgiving, examining your heart before Him, making *every effort to be found living peaceful lives that are pure and blameless..* and growing *in the grace and knowledge of our Lord and Savior, Jesus Christ.*

Walking through the Psalms

Return to Psalm 111. How do you see the Revelation picture of Jesus in this psalm? What do you see as your responsibilities while you wait to be with Him in heaven? Write out what you discover in the space below.

 Walking in Wonder

What questions do you need to ask, dear one?

*Please turn to the closing page just after today's **Walking Through Today** for a final word from the author.*

What I learned in Revelation about:		
Jesus Christ		Believers
Verse:		Verse:
		this r
(continue on next page)		

What I learned in Revelation about: (continued)		
Jesus Christ		Believers
Verse:		Verse:

Walking Through Today: Journaling the Journey

Walking Through Today: Journaling the Journey   Date:_____

In Closing:

For who is our hope or joy or crown of exultation?
Is it not even you, in the presence of our Lord Jesus at His coming?
For you are our glory and joy.
1 Thessalonians. 2:19-20

To my precious fellow *Journeyers with Jesus,*

Thank you so much for allowing me the privilege of walking with you and showing you some sights as you are *journeying with Jesus.* We've seen the vista view and hiked the trails for some close-up glimpses of the precious truths of God's Word. Through this study, I hope I've accomplished the goal of establishing for you the *basics* of Christian faith. As we are urged in the book of Jude to *contend earnestly for the faith which was once for all handed down to the saints,* we are told by Him how we will be able to do this: *But you, beloved, building yourselves up on your most holy faith, praying in the Holy Spirit, keep yourselves in the love of God, waiting anxiously for the mercy of our Lord Jesus Christ to eternal life (Jude 3, 20).* This book was written with this purpose in mind, to equip you with the God-given provisions to enable you to defend the faith, the whole Word of God.

My prayer for you is the prayer of Paul for the Philippians, *I pray that your love will overflow more and more, and that you will keep on growing in knowledge and understanding. For I want you to understand what really matters, so that you may live pure and blameless lives until the day of Christ's return. May you always be filled with the fruit of your salvation—the righteous character produced in your life by Jesus Christ—for this will bring much glory and praise to God (Phil 1:9-11 NLT).*

All for His glory,

 Conni

About the Author

As a former children's leader in Bible Study Fellowship, coordinator of the children's program for the Palm Desert, California Community Bible Study class, Precept Inductive Bible teacher for more than 13 years, and a retreat and conference speaker, Conni continues to let the Lord determine her areas of ministry. Currently, her focus is to teach and proclaim the Word primarily through *Journeying With Jesus* Ministries, and also through *Quiet Time Ministries* and the *Biblical Counseling Foundation*, all located in Palm Desert, California.

About *Journeying With Jesus* Ministries.

Journeying With Jesus is a ministry whose aim is to answer the great commission of God calling women to *journey with Jesus* in a close, personal relationship; teaching them to come alongside others to show them how to walk faithfully in their journey with the Lord, loving Him and loving others. In a retreat setting and through Bible study books, we seek to grow spiritually, bring glory to Christ, and be used by Him to draw others to Himself.

The intent of our ministry is to present the gospel, teach God's Word, and biblically counsel others how to use the provisions God has given them to journey with Him in love and truth; the emphasis being placed on the two all-encompassing yet simple commandants: to love God and love others. We want to disciple them to live and share the abundant, victorious life Jesus Christ has promised the believer.

Journeying With Jesus Ministries has three goals – three sure things we want all who come to our retreats and do our studies to know:

1. True Christianity is a relationship – not a religion. God created us for relationship with Him, relationship that is authentic, close, personal, and as unique as each person. God tells us in I John 5:20 "We know the Son of God has come and has given us understanding, in order that we might know Him who is true, and we are in Him who is true, in His Son Jesus Christ. This is the true God and eternal life." He wants us to know him as He already knows and loves us. That's relationship. We seek to help others to know Him and grow in their personal relationship with Him.

2. The Bible is 'authoritative' truth. It is the Word of the True, Living God, so it is universal in scope. That means it is the same for those around the world. It is also 'absolute'. It is God's truth so it's unaffected by situation or circumstance, proving it is not relative. There is no such thing s "a truth for you and a different truth for me." It is 'literal.' God created us to communicate in language form, so He gave us His Word to be understood as we would any language. It's simple – it says what it means and means what it says. It is also sufficient. II Timothy 3:16-17 assures us in His Word are all the answers, guidance and direction we need to live godly, victorious lives while we are *journeying with Jesus.* We desire to teach those God brings our way the truth and how to study its principles and know its promises for themselves.

3. And thirdly, we desire for all who come to *Journeying With Jesus* functions to know how much God loves them! As Jesus said in John 14 and 17, God loves His own just as He loves Jesus. That's perfectly and unconditionally. There is no merit system and nothing can separate His children from His love. We, as the Team, seek to love others with the love of Jesus, ministering to them and showing them God's way faithfully, so they might realize just how much the Father loves them and how unconditional is His love. Then, it's His job, through the Word and by His Spirit, to transform their hearts.

Journeying With Jesus Ministries seeks, through relationships with others, to show the love of God by teaching the truth and loving with His love. We do this in retreat settings and through Bible studies, ministering as the Lord gives opportunity.

Journeying With Jesus
Statement of Faith

THE SCRIPTURES
We believe in the divine inspiration and supreme authority of the sixty-six books of the Bible. The Bible alone is verbally inspired and completely inerrant in the original manuscripts and is sufficient for all matters of faith and conduct. We believe that all the Scriptures were designed for our practical instruction. Every believer has the ability to interpret the Scriptures under guidance of the Holy Spirit when interpreted in its normal, historical, grammatical, and contextual sense. *Deuteronomy 4:2; Psalm 19:7; 119:160; Proverbs 30:6; John 16:6-13; John 17:17; I Corinthians 2:12-14; II Timothy 3:16-17; II Peter 1:3-4, 20-21; Revelation 22:18-19.*

THE TRINITY
We believe that God eternally exists in three Persons – the Father, the Son, and the Holy Spirit – and that these three are one God, having precisely the same nature, attributes, perfections, and worthy of precisely the same homage, confidence, and obedience. Each member of the Triune Godhead is jointly involved in the plan of redemption for lost and sinful mankind. *Deuteronomy 6:4; 33:27a; Psalm 90:1-2; Matthew 3:16-17; 28:19-20; John 14:16-18; II Corinthians 13:14; Ephesians 4:4-6; Hebrews 1:8-12; 7:24-25; 9:14; I Peter 1:1-2.*

GOD THE FATHER
We believe that God the Father is spirit, infinite, eternal, and unchangeable in His being, power, holiness, justice, goodness, and truth. We believe that He is the Creator of all that is, that He concerns Himself mercifully in the affairs of men, that He saves from sin and spiritual death all who come to Him through Jesus Christ and He hears and answers their prayers. *Matthew 6:8-15; 7:11; 23:9; John 4:24; 14:6-13; Galatians 4:6; I John 5:13-15.*

JESUS CHRIST
We believe that the Lord Jesus Christ, the Son of God, is preexistent and complete deity, Creator of all, begotten by the Holy Spirit and born of the virgin Mary. He is both fully God and fully man. In the flesh, He lived a sinless life and died on the cross as a substitutionary sacrifice for the sins of mankind. We believe in the bodily resurrection of our Lord, His ascension into Heaven, and His presence there as our Intercessor. He is the Savior and the Head of the church. *Isaiah 7:14; 9:6-7; Matthew 1:23; Luke 1:35; John 1:1-4, 14; 10:30; 20:30-31; Romans 1:4; 3:22-28; 4:25; 8:11, 34; I Corinthians 15:1-8; II Corinthians 5:21; Ephesians 1:7; Colossians 1:15-17; Hebrews 4:14-15; 8:1; 9:28; I John 2:1.*

THE HOLY SPIRIT
We believe that the Holy Spirit is a person, that He is God, that He possesses all the divine attributes, that He is the Interpreter of the infallible Word of God, that He baptizes and indwells all believers at the moment of their salvation, that He empowers believers to live victoriously and gifts them for ministry, that He convicts the world of sin, righteousness, and judgment, and that it is the responsibility of every believer to be filled with (i.e. put himself under control of) the Holy Spirit. He is our Comforter, Counselor, and Revealer of Jesus Christ. *John 14:16-17, 26; 16:7-15; Acts 1:8; 4:31; 5:3-4; Romans 8:9-13; I Corinthians 2:9-16; 3:16; 12:13; II Corinthians 3:18; Galatians 5:16, 22-23; Ephesians 3:16; 4:30; 5:18; I John 2:18-27.*

MAN

We believe that man was created in the image of God. Because of Adam's sin, mankind incurred both physical and spiritual death. We believe that all human beings are sinners and separated from God because of their inherent sin nature, which makes each individual prone to commit sinful acts. We believe that man is unable to save himself. We believe in eternal life for the believer and eternal punishment for the unbeliever. *Genesis 1:26-27; 3:1-19; Proverbs 20:9; Isaiah 64:6; John 5:28-29; 6:40; Romans 1:18; 3:9-12, 23; 5:12-19; 6:23; I Corinthians 15:51-52; Ephesians 2:1-3:12; Titus 3:5; Hebrews 9:27; II Peter 3:7; Revelation 20:11-15.*

SALVATION

We believe that Jesus Christ died as a substitutionary sacrifice for our sins and that salvation is a gift of God brought to man by grace and received by personal faith in Jesus Christ. We believe that no works, such as water baptism, prayer, or faithful service, are to be added to believing as a condition of salvation. Jesus Christ is the only answer for mankind's helpless spiritual condition. *Isaiah 53:2-12; John 3:16; 10:17-18; 14:6; Acts 4:12; 13:38-39; Romans 5:6, 8; II Corinthians 5:21; Galatians 3:13; Ephesians 1:7; 2:8-9; I Timothy 2:5-6; Hebrews 10:10-14; I Peter 1:18-19; 3:18; I John 4:10.*

ASSURANCE AND SECURITY OF SALVATION

We believe that a believer can be certain of his salvation, which comes as a free gift of God's grace. Our assurance of salvation is based on God's promises not on man's works. Good works are a loving response to God for our salvation. They are prepared by God for us so that we should walk in them. *John 3:36; 5:24; 6:39-40; 10:28-29; 17:24; Romans 5:1; 8:1, 38-39; Ephesians 1:13-14; 2:8-10; 4:30; I Thessalonians 5:8-9; II Timothy 1:12; 4:18; Hebrews 7:25; Jude 1:24; I John 5:13.*

THE CHURCH

We believe that the Church is a spiritual organism made up of all persons who have, through saving faith in Jesus Christ, been regenerated by the Holy Spirit. We also believe that local churches are ordained of God and organized according to the Scriptures as visible expressions of the Body of Christ in a community, and that it is His will that all who profess belief in Christ be actively involved in a local assembly of believers. We believe that Christ mandated the local church to make disciples throughout the world and to carry out spiritual discipline and restoration within the local fellowship. *Matthew 16:18; 18:15-20; 28:18-20; Acts 2:42-47; I Corinthians 1:10 (and chapters 12-13); Ephesians 1:22-23; 4:11-16; 5:21, 25-32.*

THE ORDINANCES

We believe in the symbolic ordinance of believer's baptism by immersion in obedience to the command of Christ. We believe in the ordinance of the Lord's Supper in remembrance of His atoning death and in anticipation of His coming again. All believers and only believers should share in it. The ordinances were instituted by Jesus Christ for the church and are a scriptural means of testimony to God's grace until His return. *Matthew 28:19; Acts 2:38; 8:38-39; I Corinthians 11:20-34.*

THE CHRISTIAN'S SERVICE

We believe that every Christian is responsible for loving God and loving his neighbor in the power of the Holy Spirit. It is each believer's responsibility to walk in a manner worthy of the Lord and to please Him in all respects, bearing fruit in every good work, and increasing in the knowledge of God. Every believer is to preserve the unity of the spirit in the bond of peace, conducting himself within the body with all humility and gentleness, with patience, showing forbearance to one another in love. We believe that every Christian has received at least one spiritual gift at the point of salvation by the will and distribution of the Holy Spirit. A spiritual gift is a divine enablement for ministry for the building up of the Body of Christ. We believe that the local church is spiritually weak or strong in proportion to how faithfully each of its members demonstrates his love for God, other believers, and the lost, and exercises his gift or gifts. We believe that all believers will appear before the Judgment Seat of Christ to receive rewards for faithful service. *Matthew 16:27; 22:37-39 Romans 12:4-8; I Corinthians 3:10-15; 12:4-31; II Corinthians 5:10; Ephesians 4:1-13; Colossians 1:10-11; 3:23-24; I Peter 4:10.*

THE FUTURE

We believe that Christ's return for His church can happen at any time and that this "blessed hope" has vital bearing on the personal life and service of the believer. We believe that His second coming will be personal, visible, and glorious. We believe He will raise the dead and bring salvation and judgment to completion. *Isaiah 11:1-12; Acts 1:11; I Corinthians 15:42-55; I Thessalonians 4:13-18; Titus 2:13; I John 3:2-3; Revelation 19:11-21; 20:1-4.*

END NOTES

[1] Tozer, A.W. Reprinted from page 18 *The Pursuit of God* by A.W. Tozer, copyright © 1982, 1993 by Zur Ltd. Used by permission of WingSpread Publishers, a division of Zur Ltd., 800.884.4571.

[2] Barnhouse, Donald Gray, *Let Me Illustrate That* copyright © 1967, page 324, Fleming H. Revell, a division of Baker Publishering Group

[3] Tozer, A.W. Reprinted from page 30 *The Pursuit of God* by A.W. Tozer, copyright © 1982, 1993 by Zur Ltd. Used by permission of WingSpread Publishers, a division of Zur Ltd., 800.884.4571.

[4] Spurgeon, Charles Haddon *Morning and Evening* October 1 Morning Reading, Public Domain

[5] Chambers, Oswald - taken from *My Utmost for His Highest* by Oswald Chambers, © 1935 by Dodd Mead & Co., renewed •1963 by the Oswald Chambers Publications Assn., Ltd. Used by permission of Discovery House Publishers, Box 3566, Grand Rapids MI 49501. All rights reserved.

[6] Bilbrough, Dave, *I am a New Creation*, © ThankYou Music, Licence 268535 All Rights Reserved. Used by Permission. CCLI song #48425

[7] Whittle, Daniel, song title: *I Know Whom I Have Believed*, Public Domain

[8] Spurgeon, Charles Haddon as printed on page 8 in *Bible Doctrines for Today,* a Beka Book, Pensacola Christian College, Pensacola, FL quote is Public Domain

[9] Tozer, A. W. Used by permission. Reprinted from pages 9-10, *The Pursuit of God* by A.W. Tozer, copyright © 1982, 1993 by Zur Ltd. Used by permission of WingSpread Publishers, a division of Zur Ltd., 800.884.4571.

[10] *Read Your Bible* 'selected quote' as printed in *Bible Doctrines for Today* a Beka Book, Pensacola Christian College, Pensacola, FL page 74

[11] Cowman, Mrs. Charles, *Streams in the Desert*, June 6th reading Copyright © 1928, 1965 by Cowman Publications, Public Domain

[12] Cowman, Mrs. Charles, *Streams in the Desert,* January 4th reading, Copyright © 1928, 1965 by Cowman Publications, Public Domain

[13] Bounds, E. M., from *A Place Called Heaven* p. 68, © 1985, rev 2003. Used by permission of the publisher (www.whitakerhouse.com), Whitaker House Publishers, New Kensington, PA 15068

[14] Spurgeon, Charles Haddon, *Morning and Evening* January 10 Morning reading, Public Domain